The Wonderful World of Energy

The Wonderful World of

Energy

Lancelot Hogben

Doubleday and Company Inc.
Garden City, New York

Library of Congress Catalog Card Number 68-14673

Copyright © 1968 by Aldus Books Limited

Copyright © 1957 by Rathbone Books Limited (Adprint Limited)

Printed in Yugoslavia

Contents

Certain words and phrases in this book are followed by the symbol☞. Whenever you see this symbol it means that you can look up the word or phrase in the alphabetical glossary at the end of the book and find more information or a fuller definition of the term.

1 Making the Most of Muscles

At one time or another, most of us have indulged in pleasant daydreams of a tropical island paradise where there is always bathing and sunshine without the need for distasteful effort. In the real world, there has never been such an escape from work—especially when modern men first appeared, some 25,000 years ago, as hunters and food gatherers, able to cook and to fashion rough shelters for protection against cold or against attack by beasts of prey.

These earliest men and women relied chiefly on the brute force of their own muscles; yet around them there were bountiful sources of power: flowing and falling water, the heat of the sun, the wind, natural fuel, the pressure of the air, the thunderstorm, the earth's magnetic field, and, in some few places, volcanoes and hot springs.

Men and women of the Old Stone Age made use of some of these, but exploited none fully. They could use fire to cook, to bake pottery, and to create an artificial climate within the cave or the hut; the buoyancy and flow of water to carry logs or canoes downstream; and the elastic recoil of a twig or thin shaft of bone to propel missiles in the hunt.

About 20,000 years passed before people in the Middle East learned the use of fire to separate copper and tin from their ores. By then, they had already harnessed the wind as a substitute for the paddle and the oar. The use of metals gave man the means of making better tools, and with better tools and large-scale building came greater reliance on two simple devices, which we may call machines.

One was the slope, the other the sled. Both rely on human effort as a source of power. Their usefulness depends on the fact that the engines of the human body cannot do more than a certain amount of work in a certain time.

Though it may be too exhausting to lift a block of stone through a single foot vertically, it is not too exacting to move it through the same vertical height up a gentle slope. We then accomplish the same task

Early man wrested a living from the land by the brute force of his muscles.

successfully by giving ourselves more time. It may be too exhausting to keep a large load on the move across rough ground, but possible to do so by setting it on a carrier with smooth edges. We waste less work generating heat by friction and we slow down the rate at which our muscles have to work.

The 5000-year period between the beginnings of civilization in Egypt and the discovery of the New World by Columbus covers by far the largest slab of recorded history. It witnessed great progress in writing, mathematics, astronomy, geography, architecture, metallurgy, and navigation. Man came to rely on utilizing the strength of beasts of burden—ox, ass, horse, and camel; but he was slow in learning how to exploit other natural sources of power.

Before the beginning of the Christian era, however, mankind had perfected several new devices to ration the output of human or animal work, chief among them being the wheel, the lever☞, the pulley, and the capstan. Like the sled, the wheel reduces friction. Like the slope, the lever, pulley, and capstan make it possible for man or beast to accomplish an otherwise too-difficult task by allowing more time in which to do it.

So it is useful to have a word for the rate at which the human or animal body or any other engine performs work☞. Engineers use the word "power" in just this sense. By power they mean so much work done in so much time.

While slave labor was cheap, wealthy people with leisure to study had little daily contact with the world's work and little curiosity about how simple machines change the rate of work. But there was a short period when Greek-speaking mathematicians probed a little into the costing of effort☞. This was between 300 and 100 B.C.

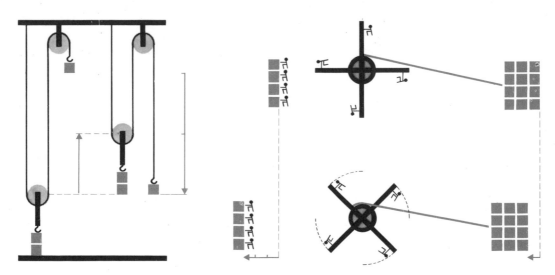

The pulley, left, uses a 1-ton weight to pull rope-end down 2 feet and thus to raise a 2-ton weight 1 foot. The capstan, right, enables four men who can shift 400 lb 3 yards, to shift 1200 lb 1 yard with just the same effort.

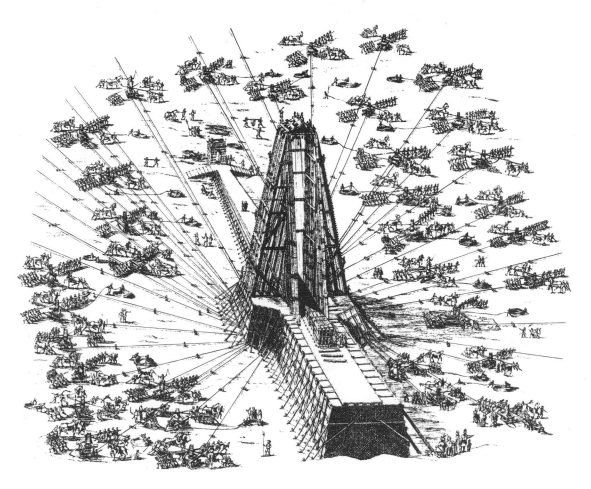

Moving a 100-ton stone column with only pulleys, capstans, and muscle-power.

During that period, Archimedes☞ discovered what we call the Law of the Lever. Two loads A and B balance when the scale-pan weight of A multiplied by its distance from the fulcrum is the same as the scale-pan weight of B multiplied by *its* distance from the fulcrum. The same principle applies to the pulley and to the capstan.

We can see a new meaning in it if we ask ourselves what is a straight-forward way of measuring work. When we lift the same load through a greater height or lift a heavier load through the same height, we do more work. So we may take as a measure of work the load multiplied by the height. The Principle of Archimedes then signifies that the lever stays poised when the human arm expends the same amount of work in a small shift at one end as does the load itself in a corresponding shift at the other end.

In the third century B.C. Archimedes designed levers and grabs to up-end Roman ships when they besieged his home town of Syracuse in Sicily. Eighteen hundred years later Domenico Fontana moved and set up in Rome itself a colossal stone column. His only machines were pulleys and capstans. The only source of available power was the muscular effort of men and horses.

Some six centuries after the time of Archimedes, Rome became Christian. The gladiatorial show went out. Slavery declined. Life and toil were no longer cheap. In the northern regions of Europe, where Christianity got a footing about A.D. 700—when the Moslems who had overrun Africa were ready to conquer Spain—outbreaks of plague took heavy toll of the working population. By sheer necessity, man began to make better use of nature's gifts.

The ancient civilizations of Mesopotamia had long since employed waterwheels of a sort, for irrigation; but Europe now began to use mills driven by falling water to grind corn, to drive circular saws, and to pump water from mines. The Moslems had crude windmills by about A.D. 800; but the windmills that began to appear in the Low Countries and along the eastern coast of Britain during and after the Crusades were of improved design, with movable turrets to catch the wind from all directions. In making them, as in making water mills, craftsmen became skilled in the use of cogwheels for gearing. Meanwhile, the art of smelting metals for warfare progressed. New and larger iron foundries multiplied the demand for fuel.

Several different civilizations of Asia and southern Europe have laid claim to the discovery of the magnetic compass, but it was certainly in the sunless seas of the North that seamen first had to come to terms with its vagaries. The direction of the compass needle changes from place to place, especially around Greenland and Iceland, familiar to Viking navigators. To steer through cloudy, starless nights in such regions, mariners had to learn just where it did point—by no means always, or anywhere exactly, north.

By now some people were beginning to learn that you can make a bar of soft iron into a magnet by rubbing it with lodestone, the natural magnet of the mariner's compass. For at least 1000 years, men had known that amber attracts dust and other fine particles when rubbed; but electricity☞, from the Greek word *electron* for amber, was otherwise unknown. The thunderstorm was still seen simply as an act of God.

Between A.D. 500 and 1500 practice had vastly outrun theory. Throughout the Middle Ages men continued to use three of the oldest devices for economizing human effort—the slope, the siphon, and the pump—without a clue about how to cost the effort saved.

There was no clue until they had the tools. To understand how the slope gears down the power output of the engines of the human or of the animal body, we need to be able to measure short intervals of time. To understand how the siphon or the pump works, we need to know that the air exerts pressure under its own weight; and this was very difficult to realize until there was cheap glass.

In the Middle Ages iron foundries multiplied, making heavy demands on fuel.

2   Getting to Grips with Gravity

School books often speak of the century before Columbus as a century of Renaissance, or rebirth. In fact, it was the century in which northern Europe first emerged from barbarism through the spread of new knowledge from the Moslem world, which had harvested the learning of the Greeks, the number-lore of the Hindus, and many of the discoveries of the Chinese, including paper-making and gunpowder. From the Moslem universities of Spain new knowledge of astronomy, geography, and the art of navigation filtered into the more backward North during the three centuries before Europe knew of the New World.

Meanwhile, windows of transparent glass were changing the houses of the more prosperous merchant classes of England and Germany. Glass windows made winter study practicable. (It had not been easy in castles whose windows were merely open slits admitting single shafts of light through massive stone walls.) In the generation before Columbus set sail, printing from movable type was bringing books within reach of people who had previously had no access to the written word. The printing press was also turning out nautical almanacs for master pilots.

Among the communities of antiquity, where there were slaves to do the strenuous or unpleasant work, mining was a topic about which scholars knew and cared nothing. But in Europe deep-shaft mining was the work of free men, proud of their craft. At a time when glass vessels were relatively abundant for the first time, the problem of pumping water to prevent the flooding of mines forced itself on the attention of gentleman scholars, with no loss of dignity to themselves. You may suspect that air has weight, but only when you have a glass tube can you watch *how* the air exerts pressure on, and affects the motion of, a column of liquid. The siphon and the pump then cease to be a mystery.

The Moslems had invented a sundial that recorded time in equal intervals; but in the gray north of Britain and Germany sundials were only occasionally of use as time recorders. Though the churches that

A Renaissance gunners' manual shows how gravity affects a flying cannonball.

A 16th-century sundial has dials for five time-systems, Eastern and Western.

A 19th-century painting shows Galileo experimenting with balls rolling down a slope, in order to compare the acceleration of lighter and heavier bodies.

nursed the invention of clocks still exhibited sundials to check their accuracy when the weather was favorable, crude clocks with geared wheels now, and for the first time, did their job. Clockmakers, conscious of the defects of their wares, were eager to sell a better product.

In China, whence it had come, gunpowder for crackers had been a harmless plaything. In Europe it was now the sinews of war. A new branch of military science was growing up: how to track the path of the cannonball. This new interest in the study of matter in motion thus coincided with the emergence of a new instrument for measuring time in short intervals.

In the days of bow-and-arrow warfare, the mounted archer had learned the hard way that the speed and direction of his horse affected the track of the missile. The bow-spring propels the arrow in one direction at a certain speed. The motion of the horse pushes it in another direction at a different speed. The arrow flies in a direction that depends on both these circumstances.

The great Italian scientist Galileo☞ was probably one of several who first saw how to analyze the motion of a cannonball in archery terms. The recipe is: make a scale diagram of how far it will move in a fixed interval of time along the straight path set by the muzzle, and how far it will fall earthward during the same period.

Actually, no one had yet studied how bodies do gain speed in falling. Most people lazily assumed that heavy ones necessarily fall more quickly than lighter ones. Galileo dropped simultaneously two cannonballs, one a hundred times as heavy as the other, from the Leaning Tower of Pisa. They landed at the same time, showing that the gain of speed (acceleration☞) in the same time is the same for both.

Galileo had no instrument good enough for measuring acceleration in a vertical fall; but he reasoned rightly that two cannonballs of different size should also have equal acceleration when rolling down the same smooth slope. So he experimented on how they do so, timing the speed with a homemade water clock.

His records disclosed a simple rule connecting the time taken and the distance traveled. On any slope, however steep, a ball rolls four times as far in two seconds as in one, nine times as far in three seconds as in one, and so on. In short, the distance varies with the square of the time.

Since bodies roll more quickly if the slope is steeper, the distance traveled depends on the angle of the slope. Galileo's records showed how much, and from them it was possible to work out how much a heavy body gains speed when the slope is as steep as possible—that is, when it falls vertically. It does so at a fixed rate. At sea level, this is almost exactly 32 feet per second in a second.

With this knowledge we find no difficulty in plotting the path of the cannonball. Under its own muzzle velocity it proceeds in a straight line determined by the tilt of the cannon; if air friction is negligible, as is true enough of the slow-moving cannonballs of Galileo's time, its speed in that direction is unchanged. All this time it is falling vertically, gaining speed at a fixed rate.

A scale diagram shows that it follows the curved track we call a *parabola*.

Galileo's discoveries about acceleration also cleared up the mystery of the slope, about which his predecessors had already found something that the ancients did not know. On a slope twice as long as its vertical height, a load of 200 lb just balances a load of 100 lb hanging vertically.

On a slope twice as long as its vertical height, the cannonball gains speed half as quickly as it does when falling vertically. Thus we see that two bodies balance one another if the mass of one multiplied by the rate at which it gains speed when released is equal to the mass of the other multiplied by the rate at which *it* gains speed when released.

In costing power, we therefore have to bring in a new notion of weight. What we loosely call the "weight" of a body is the product of two factors: its scale-pan weight, called *mass*☞, and its *acceleration*, i.e. the rate at which it gains speed when free to move under gravity, vertically or down a slope.

Galileo got to grips with why a pump fails to raise water more than about 30 feet when his own pump failed. The explanation depends on the fact that air has weight. Galileo's experiments with falling bodies had led him to suspect this, when no one else as yet did so.

He had established that all heavy compact bodies gain speed at almost exactly the same rate when falling through air. Like everyone else, he also knew that a feather falls more slowly than a stone, and that a toy balloon, in his day an air-filled pig's bladder, will dance in air. Like others, he knew too that in water some things fall fast, some slowly, and others float. Archimedes had long since found a clue to why they do so. He found that any solid body when immersed in water displaces a volume of water equal to its own volume, and loses scale-pan weight equal to that of the water displaced. Thus a ball five times as dense as water loses a fifth of its weight when placed in water; one three times as dense loses a third of its weight; and one of equal density loses all its weight.

Archimedes' discovery takes on a new meaning when we think of weight in Galileo's way—as a product of mass and acceleration. If we mean by mass the fixed amount of matter in each of them, none of the balls in our example undergoes a change in mass when placed in water; but all undergo a change in weight. The only possible explanation is that they do not gain speed at the same rate when falling in water. If all three were free to fall through air they would all accelerate at the rate of approximately 32 feet per sec². If free to fall in water the first

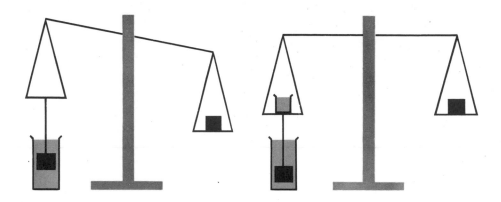

Bodies of equal scale-pan weight do not balance if one is in water. But they will balance if the lefthand pan holds volume of water equal to that displaced.

body loses a fifth of its acceleration, the second loses a third, and the third loses the whole. The third body, with no acceleration, floats.

If we now assume that air has weight and gives buoyancy, just as water does, the behavior of a falling stone and an inflated pig's bladder no longer puzzles us. The stone is many times as dense as air. So the air it displaces reduces its acceleration by only a minute fraction. The inflated bladder has roughly the same density as air. So the air it displaces reduces its acceleration to a little above zero.

A year after Galileo died in 1642, his pupil Evangelista Torricelli☞ proved that air does have weight. He held a long glass cylinder horizontally in a trough of mercury while it filled. He then raised the closed end gradually while keeping the open end under the mercury in the trough. At first the cylinder remained brimful; but each time he raised it beyond the height of about 30 inches, the mercury began to descend, leaving an entirely empty space—a vacuum—above it. The only reasonable explanation is that the weight of air on the mercury in the trough is just enough to balance that of a column of mercury 30 inches high, whose weight is equivalent to a column of water 30 feet high.

Because air, like water, is a form of matter, bodies falling through it encounter friction☞. This slows down their speed to an extent that depends on how large a surface, relative to their bulk, comes into contact with the air. Bulk for bulk a feather exposes vastly more surface than a coin. The invention of the vacuum pump made it possible to exhaust the air from a glass cylinder. One can then see that in empty space a coin and a feather fall at the same speed.

Crossing the Atlantic westward, mariners of Galileo's time now needed a reliable way of finding longitude at sea. For every 15° a seaman sails westward from his home port he sees the sun at its noonday height one hour later than if he had stayed at home; for every 15° eastward, one hour earlier. If he knows home-port time as well as local time, he can thus work out his longitude. But no clock was yet capable of keeping in time with the home port during a long voyage.

Galileo discovered that a pendulum of fixed length swings through a small arc in a fixed time; but this is true only at a fixed location. Because its motion depends on the pull of gravity, which varies with latitude and altitude, the same pendulum swings at a different pace in different places. Though a good enough regulator for stationary clocks, it is therefore useless for regulating clocks that must travel.

Men who sailed in the Ark Royal (top), and in other ships of Galileo's day, had no better instrument for finding longitude than the old astrolabe (left). The first reliable ships' chronometer (opposite page) was invented in 1735.

Soon after Galileo's death the hairspring device came into the picture. The swing of a hairspring wheel does not depend on acceleration under gravity but solely on the elastic recoil of the metal, which is not affected by altitude or latitude if the temperature remains the same. Eighteenth-century chronometers, which finally solved the longitude problem, employed hairspring wheels with gaps in the rim, so that the diameter—and thus the swing—did not change with variations of temperature.

In the meantime, Robert Hooke, an English scientist, had discovered an important property of coiled springs. If we suspend a pan from a metal spring and add one pound, then another, and another successively to it, the spring extends by equal amounts for each pound added up to a certain limit. By marking off the amount the spring extends for each pound added, we can make a spring balance. At one and the same place, where bodies have the same acceleration under gravity, it is a reliable instrument for weighing.

But acceleration under gravity is not the same everywhere. A ball that shows a spring-balance reading of 1 lb when hanging vertically has a mass of 1 lb and an acceleration of about 32 feet per sec². On a one-in-two slope, the same ball would have an acceleration of about 16 feet per sec² if free to fall, and shows a reading of $\frac{1}{2}$ lb. While acceleration remains unchanged we can thus use the spring balance to measure mass.

While mass remains unchanged we can use it to measure acceleration. If we tie a spring balance with a ball attached to its end to the pivot of a smooth horizontal turntable, the balance shows no reading while the turntable is motionless; the ball has mass but no acceleration. If we set the turntable spinning, the spring balance now shows a reading. Though the ball moves at constant speed it continually changes direction. In short, it has an acceleration toward the center of the turntable. Otherwise it would not move in a closed curve. It would go off in a straight line at a tangent.

The diagram below shows that this acceleration has a fixed relation to the speed of the ball and to its distance from the center of a very smooth turntable. If there is scarcely any friction to impede it, the acceleration is proportional to the speed multiplied by itself and divided by the radius.

In the days of Galileo, no cannonball would travel more than a few hundred feet horizontally or rise more than a few score feet. To regard the earth as flat, and to regard its pull (as Galileo did) as a fixed force at right angles to it, introduced an error in tracking the cannonball's flight. It was a tiny error, safe to ignore. But we cannot afford to ignore it when we are dealing with modern missiles that travel hundreds of miles and rise to great heights.

When an object goes up high enough, we can no longer ignore the error due to change of pull; experiments with pendulum or with spring balance show measurable differences even between the earth's pull at the bottom of a mountain and that at the top. If a missile goes far enough sideways, we cannot afford to neglect the earth's curvature. An object fired with force enough to send it beyond the earth's atmosphere

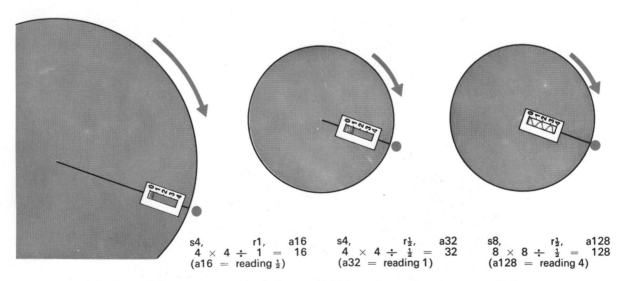

s4,	r1,	a16	s4,	r½,	a32	s8,	r½,	a128
4 × 4 ÷ 1 = 16			4 × 4 ÷ ½ = 32			8 × 8 ÷ ½ = 128		
(a16 = reading ½)			(a32 = reading 1)			(a128 = reading 4)		

A ball revolving on a very smooth turntable has an acceleration toward the center. The acceleration depends on the speed of the ball and on its distance from the center: acceleration = speed × speed ÷ radius

Testing Sea Cat, *a modern missile weapon fired from the side of a ship.*

can keep revolving around the earth indefinitely, because of the changing direction of the earth's pull at every instant in its course.

Early in the 17th century Johannes Kepler☞ discovered that the squares of the times that two planets take to circle the sun (that is, their *years*) are in the same proportion as the cubes of their average distances from the sun.

Let us take an example. The earth is 92·9 million miles from the sun, and Venus 67·5 million, and

$$(92 \cdot 9 \div 67 \cdot 5)^3 = 1 \cdot 38^3 = 2 \cdot 62$$

The earth's year is $365\frac{1}{4}$ days, and that of Venus 225 days, and

$$(365\tfrac{1}{4} \div 225)^2 = 1 \cdot 62^2 = 2 \cdot 62$$

We have learned that when a body moves in a circle, a constant force must pull it toward the center; and that its acceleration toward the center is equivalent to the square of its speed divided by the radius of the circle. Its speed, of course, is the circumference of the circle divided by the time of its revolution; and the circumference is proportional to the radius. So the acceleration is proportional to the radius divided by the square of the time. Kepler's rule must therefore mean that the pull of the sun on two different planets is inversely proportional to the squares of their distances from the sun.

It occurred to several people that the pulls of all bodies on each other follow Kepler's rule—for instance, that of earth and moon, and that of earth and cannonball. Fifty years after Kepler discovered that the planets obey the rule, Isaac Newton☞ showed that this guess is right.

The moon revolves every 654 hours at a distance of 240,000 miles from the earth's center. We can calculate from this that the earth's pull upon it is equivalent to an acceleration of $(32 \div 60)^2$ feet per second in a second. At the surface of the earth, 4000 miles from its center and thus $\frac{1}{60}$ of the distance of the moon, the acceleration is 32 feet per second in a second. So Kepler's rule holds good.

Unknowingly, Newton thus showed how to forecast the speed at which a man-made missile must move to settle in a circular orbit around

the earth. Suppose that we want our satellite☞ to circle the earth at a height of 800 miles—that is, 4800 miles from the earth's center. We can compare it with the moon, by using Kepler's rule, which tells us:

(Moon dist. ÷ Satellite dist.)^3 = (Moon rev. time ÷ Satellite rev. time)^2

If we put in the right figures, we get:

$$(240,000 \div 4800 \text{ miles})^3 = (654 \div \text{Satellite rev. time in hours})^2$$

From this we can work out that the satellite revolution time will be about 1·85 hours.

At 4800 miles from the earth's center the satellite will travel 30,144 miles in each complete revolution, and must have a velocity of 16,294 mph. It must therefore be projected so that it is moving horizontally with this velocity when 800 miles from the earth's surface. The satellite will then continue to circle the earth almost indefinitely, without any further boost.

Opposite page, a satellite is launched by a giant rocket that provides the thrust it needs to escape the earth's atmosphere. Above, a photograph taken from one of America's Gemini spacecraft shows the other craft orbiting the earth.

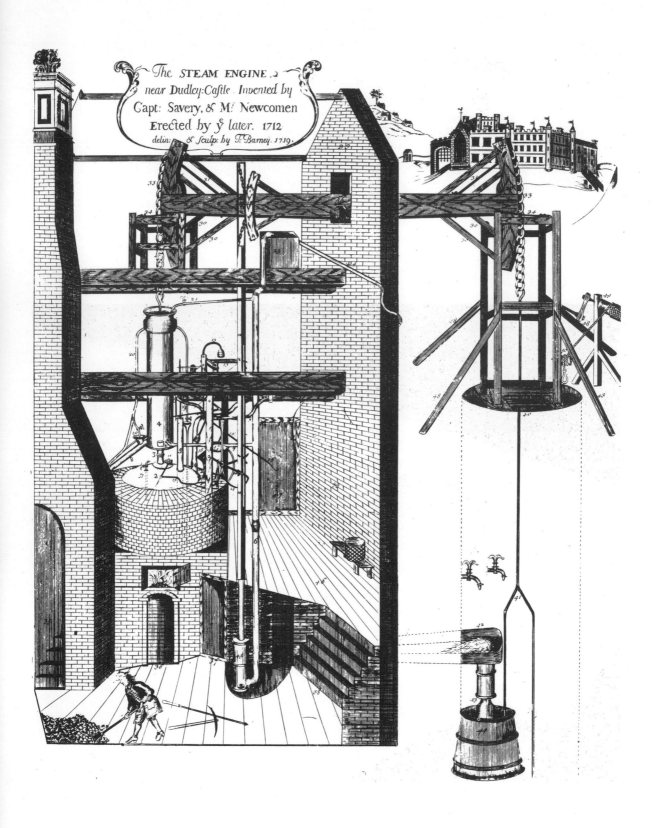

The STEAM ENGINE near Dudley-Castle Invented by Capt: Savery, & Mr. Newcomen Erected by ye later. 1712

delin: & sculp: by T. Barney. 1719.

3 Harnessing Heat

When Newton showed that the same force that makes the cannonball fall to earth keeps the moon in its curved path, there was no prospect of launching a man-made satellite. Theory was far ahead of practice. Better clock design was the main technical advance of Newton's century and the most impressive use of nature's own power resources was a giant water-driven pump at Marly, near Paris. The current of the river Seine propelled its multiple wheels to raise water to a high tower from which an aqueduct carried it nearly half a mile to the palace of the king at Versailles.

During Newton's lifetime, water and wind were the only natural sources of power available for manufacturing processes; but the study of air pressure and pump mechanisms had already suggested how to use heat as a source of power. Before Newton's death, there were steam engines of a sort in action. No one could have foreseen how steam would revolutionize industry a century later.

Today, we think of a steam engine as a device in which the pressure of steam drives a piston or turbine☞; but the earliest engines did not use steam in this way. When steam condenses at atmospheric pressure, the volume of water produced is relatively small. So we can make a partial vacuum by using steam to displace the air in a vessel and then cooling it to make it condense. Such a partial vacuum will suck in air like a pump in reverse. Several inventors saw that it could be useful to pump water out of mines. The most successful of them was Thomas Newcomen, who completed his engine in 1712.

The essential parts of Newcomen's engine were a boiler and, vertically above it, a piston attached to a pump handle. Below the piston a tube admitted a fine jet of cold water at the end of the forward stroke. This created a partial vacuum by condensing the steam in the boiler and in the piston chamber. The weight of the air then pressed the piston down. Each time this happened, the water in the boiler cooled below boiling

The first effective steam engine, invented by Newcomen and erected in 1712.

point; and it was necessary to bring it to the boil and so produce a new output of steam before the process could repeat itself.

After the installation of the first Newcomen engine as a pump to drain a deep tin mine in Cornwall, England, half a century passed before there was any further advance toward fuller use of steam power in industry.

Many people speak of James Watt☞ as the inventor of the steam engine. What is true is that Watt made the first steam engine that could turn the wheels of industry. For 50 years before Watt succeeded, Newcomen's engine had been in use; but it had one use only—it could pump water out of mines that would otherwise have been flooded. Throughout the first half of the 18th century, watermills and windmills were indeed the only engines available for driving heavy machinery.

In 1763 Watt, then mathematical instrument maker to the University of Glasgow, was asked to repair a model Newcomen engine that belonged to the Natural Philosophy class. While doing so, he soon realized what the great drawback of Newcomen's engine was.

It wasted fuel in the process of reheating the piston chamber each time the water jet cooled the chamber to condense the steam. He therefore added a separate chamber with a pump to suck in steam and cool it until it condensed. Since there was no appreciable cooling of the boiler or piston, one result was a very considerable saving on fuel. There was also less time lag between two strokes.

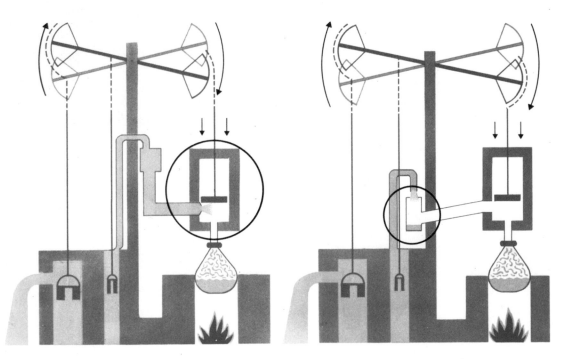

In Newcomen's engine, cold water condensed the steam in the piston chamber, which had to be reheated.

In James Watt's engine, steam was condensed in a separate chamber, so that the piston chamber remained hot.

A steam engine so much more economical than that of Newcomen attracted the interest of two Birmingham businessmen who foresaw that Watt's invention might be useful in manufacturing industries. Boulton and Roebuck went into partnership with Watt to make steam engines with separate condensers. The economy and speed of the new engine attracted many customers in the mines. For several years the new firm did not sell its engines outright. It worked on a premium basis. The partners supplied a Watt engine on condition that they would receive one third of the savings on fuel made by replacing its predecessor over a period of 25 years. After that, the engine would belong to the user.

Like the Newcomen engine, the ones that replaced it made no use of the direct pressure of steam. When the steam condensed in the separate chamber, it created a partial vacuum in the piston chamber. The pressure of the air itself forced the piston down and the weight of the working arm provided the impulse of the forward stroke. It was the atmosphere that did the work, and people spoke of such machines as atmospheric engines.

In 1777 Watt's first pumping engine was at work in a Cornish tin mine; but it was clear enough that it could do other work. Newcomen's engine had been too sluggish to keep a wheel in motion. Watt's engine was not, and Britain was eager to exploit a source of power with so many advantages over wind or water. In 1780 James Pickard patented the crank for converting the to-and-fro action of the piston into rotary

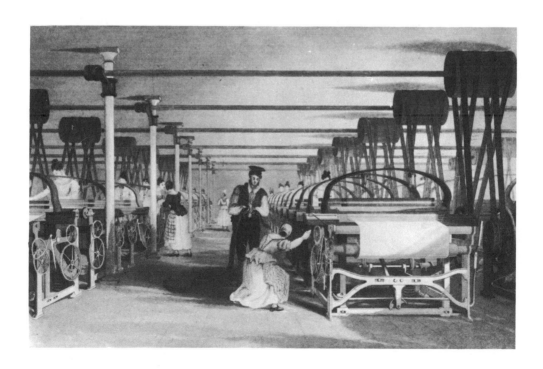

More efficient steam engines meant that cotton and woolen goods—formerly woven by hand—could be mass-produced on power looms in steam-driven mills.

motion. This forced Watt and other newcomers in the field to use more complicated ways of making a wheel turn. Among others, the most picturesque is the Sun and Planet gear.

Workshops that used water power had employed few people and could not be built near to one another. Steam engines equipped with wheels made it possible to build factories on a large scale anywhere with access to fuel. Steam-driven mills to weave cotton and woolen goods multiplied in the coal-mining regions of Britain, and Britain became, temporarily, the workshop of the world.

We have seen that Britain was well on her way to becoming a manufacturing nation in 1800. Between 1775 and 1800 Watt's company alone supplied nearly 500 steam engines to industries and municipalities; but in large sections of the country water power was still in use because abundant. Steam engines need coal; and the carriage of coal from mines to where there was a use for it was a slow and expensive process. The new mechanical age needed faster, more economical transport.

So soon as the steam engine could turn a wheel, it was obvious that it could supply power for traction; but there were two problems to solve before it could carry its own weight. One was that a separate condenser needs a constant source of cold water, of which it would be wasteful to store sufficient for a journey. The other was that the complicated gearing of the first rotary steam engines could not drive a wheel fast enough or smoothly enough to propel a vehicle with advantage.

28

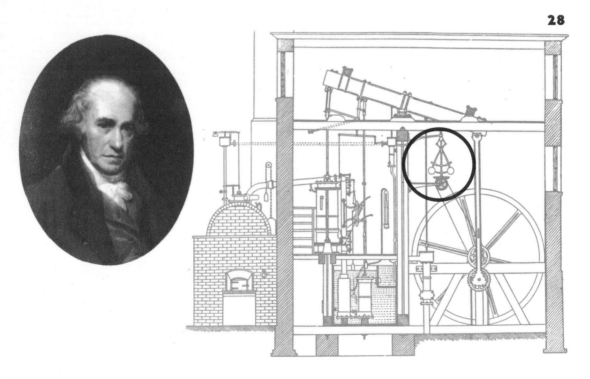

Left, portrait of James Watt. Right, Watt's double-acting steam engine of 1782. Its centrifugal governor (circled) released excess steam through a valve.

The double-acting steam engine, patented in 1781 by Hornblower and in 1782 by Watt, disposed of both these difficulties. An engine of this type does not depend on atmospheric pressure. The pressure of the steam itself acts directly on both ends of the piston. Since the steam escapes into the air, there is no need to cool the piston chamber.

Getting rid of the condenser also made faster piston action possible and therefore faster crank and wheel action; but the use of high internal pressure introduced a new hazard. Watt therefore designed the centrifugal governor to sidestep the possibility of explosion. In this device, a vertical shaft connected to the boiler turns as the steam pressure increases. When the shaft spins fast enough, two heavy balls attached to it swing out, raising a collar that opens a valve through which steam can escape harmlessly.

Mechanical transport was at last practicable. Actually, Nicholas Cugnot, a Frenchman, had already built a steam carriage in 1763; but a locomotive of this type, able to travel at about $2\frac{1}{2}$ miles per hour, could run for only 15 minutes at a time because of its small boiler. The invention of engines that make direct use of steam pressure encouraged many attempts to put steam on the roads and rivers. Richard Trevithick patented the first really successful railroad engine in 1802. This happened in England; but the first commercial passenger steamboat went into service in 1807 on the Hudson River in America. By 1812 a locomotive was hauling 30 coal wagons over a three-mile track from the coal mines to Leeds, in northern England. On September 15, 1830, a steam locomotive pulled the first public passenger train from Liverpool to Manchester. The Duke of Wellington was himself aboard to celebrate so great an occasion.

One may well ask why the designers of early locomotives, ships, and stationary steam engines employed steam to drive a piston to and fro.

George Stephenson's steam locomotive, the Caledonian, *pulling one of the first public passenger trains on the Liverpool-Manchester Railway in 1833.*

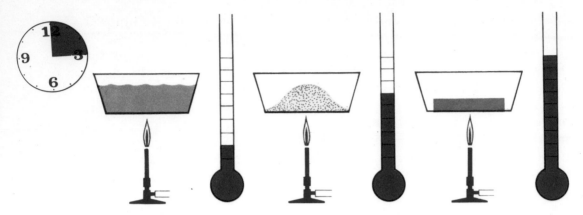

When 1 lb of water, 1 lb of sand, and 1 lb of iron are heated on the same flame, temperature of water rises 1°, that of sand 5°, and that of iron 9°.

The inventors were familiar with a simpler principle in the watermills of their own time. There the force of falling water drives the wheel directly; and in theory a jet of steam could do the same. Actually, it was necessary to solve several engineering problems before the design of a steam turbine☞ was feasible.

Mass production of steel was still in its babyhood and the technique of casting a wheel with blades of suitable design was not as yet in sight. Indeed, the steam turbine, which has largely displaced the steam piston in industry and shipping, did not go into production until a hundred years later.

When Boulton and Watt installed a new engine to replace an older steam pump, they had charged rent on fuel saved for equivalent work output. As a measure of work☞ output, Watt defined horsepower☞ as the force that can lift 33,000 pounds through one foot in one minute. The unit of power we now call a watt☞, in recognition of his researches, is 1/746 hp.

Since fuel varies in quality, the quantity of fuel burned is a very crude measure of the heat intake of an engine; even in Watt's time men of science were beginning to measure heat more precisely, for instance by finding what circumstances affect the melting of a fixed amount of ice. Having now thermometers as we know them, they had a reliable yardstick of warmth. Today, we call it temperature.

The liquid in a thermometer always rises to the same height when we immerse the bulb in boiling water at sea level. It falls to the same depth whenever we surround it with melting ice. Any two thermometers with a scale marked off between these fixed points in the same number of equal divisions, usually called degrees, will register the same scale division when placed side by side in any liquid warmer than melting ice and cooler than boiling water. On the so-called centigrade☞

scale, we label the fixed points for melting ice and boiling water as 0° and 100° (c); on the Fahrenheit☞ scale as 32° and 212° (F).

If we need a pint of warm water to melt a certain amount of ice, we need two pints of equally warm water to melt twice as much. We need less warm water to melt a fixed amount of ice than we should need of equally warm kerosine. In short, heating power depends on temperature, on the mass☞ of the material, and on its chemical nature. The unit of heat we now use is the calorie☞. This is $\frac{1}{100}$ of the heating power lost by one gram of water in cooling from 100° to 0° c (i.e. 1 calorie per gram of water per degree).

To measure heating power in calories, we need to know that the temperature drop for 100 grams of hot water is three times as great as the temperature rise of 300 grams of cold water mixed with it. If we regard the loss of calories by the hot water as equal to the gain of calories by the cold water in reaching the same end temperature, we can calculate what the end temperature will be. For instance, 100 grams of water at 70° c mixed with 300 grams at 10° c reach 25° c. The hot water drops $(70-25)°=45°$ and loses $45 \times 100 = 4500$ calories. The cold water rises $(25-10)°=15°$ and gains $15 \times 300 = 4500$ calories.

To calculate end temperature we call it T. If we mix 30 grams of water at 80° c with 3 grams at 14°, the hot water drops $(80-T)°$, losing $30(80-T)$ calories, and the cold rises $(T-14)°$, gaining $3(T-14)$ calories. If $30(80-T)=3(T-14)$, $33T=2442$ and $T=74°$.

The steam engine can do work only when there is fuel to supply heat. We convey this by saying that it converts heat into work. In the

Aborigines turn work into useful heat when they make fire by friction. Friction is the resistance produced by one surface rubbing against another.

same sense we know that we can convert work into heat. From earliest times people at work must have noticed that tools become hot. In everyday speech we say there is friction☞ when heat is produced by part of the effort we put into shifting a load or turning a wheel. It is man's earliest way of starting a fire.

If an engine gives a fixed work output for a fixed heat intake, it seems natural to conclude that there will also be a fixed output of heat for a fixed amount of work wasted in friction. When Newcomen invented his steam pump, this was not obvious for two reasons. The first was that people thought of heating power only in terms of what makes a body feel hotter. When they could measure hotness as temperature, men of science found that water remains at the same temperature from the time it comes to the boil until it boils away. There seems to be no heat to show for the fuel consumed. Somewhere heat seems to be lost.

Watt's great teacher, Black of Glasgow, showed that no real loss occurs. When water at 100° c changes into steam at 100° c, the steam stores heating power that we can use to raise the temperature of cold water. When we do so, we find that the steam imparts to the water an amount of heat exactly equal to that which *seems* to be lost while the boiling water is changing into steam. When we actually measure the stored heating power of steam in this way, we find that it takes about six times as many calories to turn boiling water into steam as to bring the same quantity of water from room temperature up to boiling point.

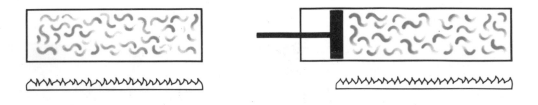

Steam in a sealed vessel is unable to expand (lefthand diagrams); when heat is applied, the temperature rises sharply. When the same amount of heat is applied to an equal volume of steam in a piston chamber (righthand diagrams) the temperature rise is less, but the steam expands and pushes the piston.

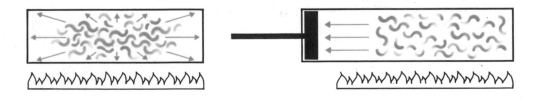

Opposite page, a steam locomotive, however efficient, must always lose some of its heat in the form of steam. We can never convert all heat into work.

While thermometers were less sensitive than those of today, scientists had a second reason for doubting that there is a fixed heat-work exchange rate. It then seemed that a cataract generates no heat in friction with the rocks. In 1830, James Joule of Manchester could detect no difference in temperature between the top and bottom of a waterfall, however large. With a modern thermometer we can detect a difference but it is very small.

One of Joule's experiments showed why. He used a falling weight to turn a paddle in a vessel filled with water and well protected from heat loss. A weight of 1 lb has a pulling power of 32 units measured in feet and pounds (acceleration ☞ × mass). It does 320 units of work in falling 10 feet. In doing so, it raises the temperature of 1 lb of water by less than $\frac{1}{100}°$ C.

Another way of measuring the exchange rate of work units and calorie gain is to apply equal amounts of heat to two equal quantities of steam, one in a sealed vessel and the other in a piston chamber where the piston is free to move and to lift a load. In the piston chamber, where the piston has done a measurable amount of work, the rise in temperature will be less than that in the sealed vessel. We can measure the work done by the piston in foot-pounds and find the ratio between the amount of work done and the apparent calorie deficit.

Many methods give almost exactly the same value for this fixed heat-work ratio. We thus know how much work we could accomplish if we

were able to convert all the heating power of our fuel into work. Thus our fixed heat-work ratio gives us a yardstick of efficiency.

To make the most efficient engine our aim will be to convert as much heat as possible into useful work.

When a falling weight drives a paddle wheel in a chamber of water insulated from heat loss, all there is to show for the work done by it is that the temperature has gone up. When steam in a piston chamber fails to reach the temperature to which the same quantity of fuel would raise an equal mass of steam in a sealed vessel, all there is to show for the *deficit* of heating power is the work the piston can do. The fixed ratio of heating power gained to input of work in the first case is the same as the fixed ratio of heating power deficit to output of work in the second case.

To give good value from an engine for market price, the engineer will aim to make the proportion of heating power spent in doing work as high as possible; but we cannot hope to achieve 100 per cent efficiency in this sense. Aside from the fact that some of the work the piston would otherwise do is wasted in friction, an engine must continually use some of the heating power of its fuel to bring water up to the boil and to keep it boiling under pressure.

Only a part of the heating power of the fuel can supply pressure on the piston or on the blades of the turbine. It turns out that the proportion gets higher as we raise the temperature in the boiler. Thus part of the recipe for making an engine as efficient as possible is to design its parts to stand very high pressures, and to employ proper safeguards lest stresses due to unequal expansion should cause an explosion or jam the works.

When engineers realized that their target had to be high boiler temperature, further advance to efficiency had therefore to depend on improvement of the quality of steel; and the production of steel of better quality for the purpose called for closer study of the way in which heat makes metals expand.

It is now easier to see why it was not possible to construct steam turbines more efficient than piston engines until the latter part of the 19th century, when high-quality steel was in mass production and there were new processes for molding it. With better materials at their disposal engineers could at last design efficient steam turbines, which were soon in use—like the one in the picture opposite—for large-scale production of electric power.

Had there been no work on the design of the steam turbine, there would have been a much longer delay in improving the design of waterwheels and in using them to harness the power of Niagara and other cataracts to generate electricity. How all this came about from small beginnings in the time of James Watt is the next chapter of the story of power.

Interior of a high-pressure steam turbine in use in a modern power station.

4 The Strength of the Storm

In the time of Watt, the study of electricity☞ had far to go before the possibility of power-producing generators was in sight. When the Pilgrim Fathers sailed, no one knew more about electricity than the very little the Greeks knew: that amber (*electron* in their tongue) attracts pieces of dust, chippings of feathers, and other light objects when rubbed with a dry rag, silk, or fur. Men of science in Newton's time had learned that many substances do so. In fact, all can, if provided with protection from contact with the hand. They thus learned to distinguish between insulators☞, which retain their attractive power after rubbing, and conductors, which lose it unless provided with a handle or covering of insulating material.

Germany's Otto von Guericke☞, in Newton's time, made a ball of sulfur that he could rotate with one hand and rub with the other. The ball attracted small pieces of paper as a vulcanite fountain pen will do when rubbed against the sleeve. Unexpectedly, the rubbing produced a crackle and minute visible sparks.

Here for the first time was a machine that could recreate in miniature the mystery of the thunderstorm. Encouraged by the novelty of doing so, other experimenters devised larger machines and found that they could store the power to attract in a device called the Leyden jar. When the Leyden jar releases its attractive power—or, as we now say, charge—it emits a spark and a bang. On touching the terminals at that moment, a human being receives a violent shock, struck as by lightning, though not fatally.

Among those who did most to advance the study of these phenomena in Watt's time was Benjamin Franklin, one of the Founding Fathers of the United States. Franklin was a friend of Watt, whom he visited in Birmingham. One of Franklin's achievements was the first electrical invention, a lightning conductor to protect buildings in thunderstorms. First he had to prove that a thunderstorm is a heavenly Guericke

An 18th-century experiment in producing electricity with a friction machine.

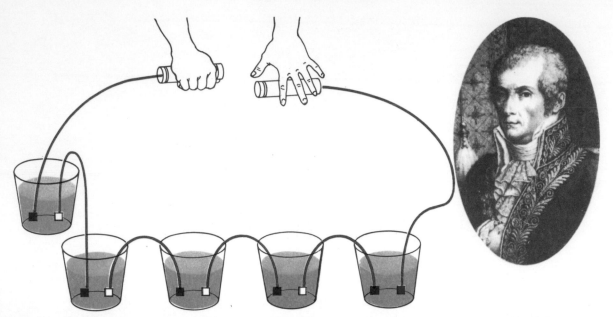

Alessandro Volta (portrait) was the first to find a source of continuous electricity. He found that chemical action between copper and zinc can produce a current.

machine. He convinced others by showing that the moist cord attached to a kite can conduct the charge from a thundercloud to earth.

Before Franklin's century ended, an accidental discovery by an Italian scientist, Luigi Galvani☞, led to the invention of a new type of generator to make thunderstorms in miniature.

He found that wires of brass and iron in contact with the leg of a freshly decapitated frog make its muscles contract. He concluded wrongly that he had discovered something new about living beings. Another Italian, Alessandro Volta☞, proved that the brass and iron were responsible for the contraction.

Volta packed, face to face, flat plates of different metals A and B, such as iron and brass or zinc and copper, between cloth pads, C, soaked in acidulated water, in the order ABCABCABC . . . AB. On touching the ends of wires connected to the first and last plates, of different metals A and B, he was able to get a powerful spark.

Volta's pile was the first chemical generator we now call a battery☞. Its simplest form, a cell, is two plates of different metals immersed in water containing salt, acid, or alkali. A series of such cells, with terminals of unlike metals connected by a copper wire, builds up a powerful battery.

Since bubbles of gas collect on the plates when a wire connects the terminals, such generators seemingly owe their peculiar powers to chemical changes. Bubbles of gas also collect around the free ends of the wires if immersed in water with a few drops of acid or grains of salt added to it.

Opposite: Davy's safety lamps (left) reduced the risk of firedamp explosions in the mines. By 1890, a few had electric lamps (right) that solved the problem.

In 1800, two English chemists, Carlisle and Nicholson, gave the 19th century a flying start by collecting the bubbles. They already knew what Watt and others had shown. An electric spark explodes in a mixture of hydrogen and oxygen with the formation of a film of water. This seemed to show that the water is a compound of hydrogen and oxygen.

If we dip the free ends of the wires from the two terminals of a battery in a vessel of water, bubbles set free at the end of one wire are bubbles of oxygen; bubbles at the end of the other are bubbles of hydrogen. The process continues until there is no water left. Only hydrogen and oxygen remain, the volume of hydrogen at all stages being twice the volume of oxygen. Nicholson and Carlisle concluded that the electric current decomposes water into its two elements, hydrogen and oxygen. These combine to form water in the ratio 2 to 1 by volume.

Sir Humphry Davy☞ found that a strong current passed through sodium hydroxide (caustic soda) and potassium hydroxide (potash) makes these substances melt and decompose, producing hitherto unknown and very light metals, in one case sodium, in the other potassium. A new chapter in chemistry unfolded, because the current will also decompose a solution of other metallic salts, depositing a film of metal on a plate connected with one battery terminal and gas bubbles on a plate connected with the other.

Davy himself constructed a lamp by bringing close together carbon rods connected with the terminals of a very large battery. He showed that a diamond burns in the spark discharge of the arc and that it forms only the same gas, called carbon dioxide, as does graphite or pure carbon.

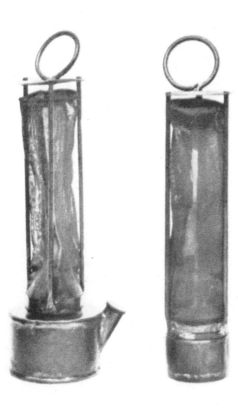

When reduced to nothing else, a diamond produces the same quantity of gas as an equal mass of graphite.

Two simple observations of what electricity can do gave the clue for using the new power source in practical machines. Simply by fiddling about, experimenters learned that wire from a battery can deflect a compass needle and can also make a magnet. All this happened by 1825. Within a few decades, the magnetic, heating, and chemical effects of electricity began to change the world.

Inventors put the magnetic effect to work on a commercial scale first in the electric telegraph, later in the telephone receiver and in the early electric motors that powered the first streetcars. They employed the heating effect successively in the carbon arc lamp, the filament lamp, cookers, fires, and electric welding devices. The chemical effect, first used in silver plating, led in time to the commercial production of magnesium and aluminum, thus paving the way for flashlight photography and for the modern aircraft industry.

From early times, men had sent signals over a distance by beacons lighted on hilltops. The discovery that a battery can deflect a compass needle or make a magnet led within a few years to two new ways of sending signals through wires. The first was the semaphore way, which uses a current to deflect a compass needle to right and left; the second was the Morse way, which lets an electromagnet buzz out long

In an automatic telegraph office of the 1870s, operators punch out messages in code on strips of paper so that they can be transmitted as pulses of electric current. A needle on a lettered dial spells out incoming messages.

"dashes" or short "dots" by attracting a vibrator in the long or short press-down of a switch. The use of electricity for signaling came just before railroads. When people traveled by horse, they had no timetable. When they built single-track railroads, with only a few loop lines where trains could pass each other, there was need for the first time to send signals over distances far beyond the sight of hilltops, to announce the time of arrival. The new battery did the job successfully and without using much power.

The new batteries could also deposit a film of metal without wearing down quickly. The 18th century had seen the development of the Sheffield-plate process, by which a layer of silver was fused onto a copper base by heating, but electroplating now got results that no one could get so cheaply in any other way. What looked like silver forks and spoons were cheap enough to produce for people who could not afford solid silver cutlery.

But light from the new arc lamp, though convenient, was also expensive. The battery that produced it soon wore out, and was not cheap to replace. Practical men therefore soon began to ask how to make a budget of costs for the new power source.

If we still lived in the days when the flow of water was the source of power for the waterwheel, it would be commonplace to measure a current of water. We can do so by weighing how much water leaves a

The electroplating bath above contains forks connected to the negative terminal of a source of direct current, and silver bars connected to the positive terminal. Action of current dissolves silver and deposits it on forks in a fine film.

pipe or reservoir in an hour, a minute, or a second. People used to watching the waterwheel at work measured what they called the electric "current" by the mass of a given metal that it deposits during a fixed period of time.

When we connect cells in series—by wiring up opposite terminals— the amount of current so measured is directly proportional to the number of identical cells in the battery, provided we keep the amount of wire in the circuit fixed. If we use the same battery and vary the length of wire, we find that we get half as much current for twice as much wire. This leads us to think of the so-called current as the ratio of two quantities. One depends on the generator, the other on the opposition of the wire to the flow of electricity.

We know that a high head of pressure increases the outflow of water from a cistern, while a narrow tube at the exit decreases it. Likewise, adding more cells in series increases the electric current and inserting a longer wire in the circuit cuts it down. The rule is simple if we use C for current, V for generator-strength (voltage), and R for resistance☞, i.e. opposition of the circuit to the flow of the current. If we measure resistance and voltage in the right units, it is $C = V \div R$.

We say a current has a strength of 1 ampere☞ when it deposits a certain fixed amount of silver for plating in one second. Having decided how much, we can decide to call the generator strength 1 volt☞ for a particular cell. We can then say that the resistance of a wire is one unit (1 ohm☞) if a generator of 1 volt produces a current of 1 ampere in it.

The resistance of a wire depends on three things: its thickness, its length, and the metal of which it is made. For any one metal, the greater the sectional area, the less the resistance; the greater the length, the greater the resistance.

Joule discovered a simple rule that tells us how much heat a current produces. The heat generated in a fixed time is always directly proportional to the current multiplied by the voltage. For fixed current, voltage is greatest where resistance is greatest. So heat produced in any part of the circuit is also greatest where resistance is greatest. Therefore a thin wire melts more quickly than a thick one. Such is the principle of the fuse.

Since there is a fixed ratio between heat and work, we can express heat production per hour, etc., as power output. Thus we measure power as current × voltage. The unit called the *watt* is the output of a circuit in which the current is 1 ampere between 1-volt terminals.

Early in the 19th century, there were many applications of the chemical, magnetic, and heating effects of the electric current. Until it was possible to make a generator less costly than the battery, some of them were little more than toys. The voltaic battery is expensive to replace, and the rate at which it wears out depends on the current used.

Using electrical pressure welding to make a joint in the wheel of a train.

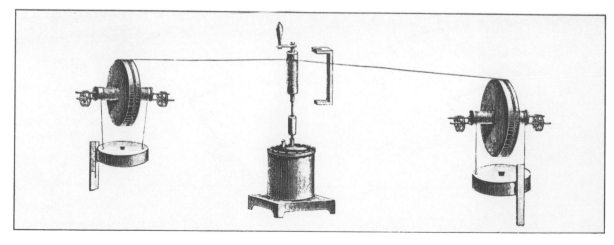

The apparatus Joule used to determine the mechanical equivalent of heat. Two weights, suspended alongside measuring scales, operated a paddle wheel in a boiler, and thus raised the temperature of the water by a measurable amount.

Silver-plating a spoon or deflecting the needle of a telegraph uses relatively little current. An arc lamp uses a lot of current and quickly exhausts a battery, and so does a motor big enough to be of use in the home or the factory.

We have seen that a battery current can cause a chemical change and is itself produced by a chemical change. When it was also clear that the battery current can deflect a magnetic needle or turn a bar of iron into a magnet, it was possible to use a current to turn a wheel. Just as the piston of the steam engine☞ regulates the valve that reverses the direction in which the pressure of the steam acts on it, the attraction of a piece of iron toward an electromagnet can operate a switch that turns off the current within its coil and turns it on in the coil of a second electromagnet. Such is the direct current motor.

It was now tempting to try out the possibility that a moving magnet can generate a current. In 1831 Davy's pupil Michael Faraday showed that it can. When we move a magnet rapidly to and fro in a coil of wire, a current flows through the coil, reversing its direction as we reverse the direction in which the magnet moves. When we know this we hold a clue to the construction of a generator at once less costly and more powerful than the battery.

If a simple loop of wire rotates between opposite poles of a magnet, the direction of the current changes at each half turn; but we can use a reversing switch, called a *commutator*, to make the current flow in one direction. We say that the first method gives an alternating current (AC☞) and the second a direct current (DC☞).

The interrupted direct current produced by the new generator, called a *dynamo*, deposits a finer film of silver for plating than does the steady current of the battery. There was thus an immediate use for it in the expanding electroplating industry of the 1830s.

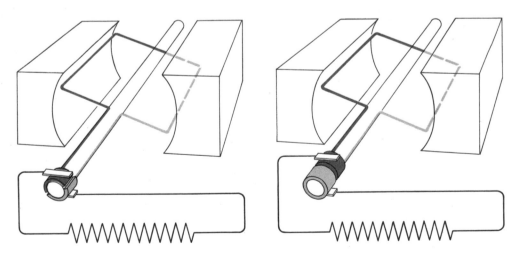

In an AC generator, left, ends of coil are connected to two metal rings, and the current changes direction at each half turn. In a DC generator, right, the ends are connected to a split ring that keeps the current flowing in one direction.

The fastest electric trains run on AC supplied by light overhead conductors.

Two things encouraged engineers to make better and larger dynamos driven by steam. One was that lighthouses were still dependent on oil; and arc lamps connected by cable to shore made storage of large quantities of oil in case of storm unnecessary. Another was that electric motors were already proving their usefulness to drive workshop tools, and to supply power for the first motorized printing press.

The dynamo came into its own when it became possible to replace permanent magnets by electromagnets energized by part of the generator current. By then another use was in sight. Around 1880 several American and British inventors used an electric current to bring a

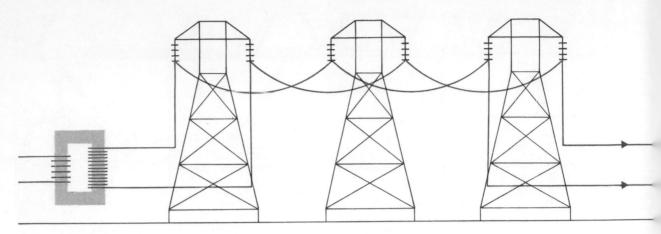

Transformers help to carry electricity from the power station to the home . . .

carbon filament to white heat in a vacuum tube, where it could not burn away. Such lamps greatly reduced the risk of fire and the labor costs involved in lighting large buildings. So the demand for electric power became still greater.

Faraday☞ in Britain and Joseph Henry in America were foremost in studying how to use magnetism to generate a current. They also made another important discovery. A coil of wire carrying an interrupted or alternating current (the primary coil) can induce a current to flow in another coil (the secondary coil) placed near it. If two coils of wire of the same thickness have the same number of loops, the voltage is the same in both. If the secondary coil has more loops than the primary, the voltage in it is proportionately higher; and if it has fewer loops, the voltage is proportionately lower. Consequently we can use an arrangement of two coils as a transformer to step up or step down voltage.

An induction coil equipped with a switch that a revolving wheel can turn on and off can deliver a spark in a closed chamber containing an explosive mixture. Coils of this kind made it possible to design the first workable internal-combustion engines.

Because it could do so many new things and because it was so easy to distribute, electricity had become vastly important by 1900; but the real source of power behind the dynamo was still steam. Dynamos were useful partly because electric power could do things it was impossible to do before, partly because it could do some jobs more economically than they could be done by older methods. Electricity could also bring power by wire from places where there was fuel to places where there were resources and people to do useful work. It was no longer necessary to transport coal from mine to factory. One could use coal to produce electricity locally and send it by wire to where it was needed.

Where electrical power was in use to do new things, the cost was least important. Where its use was mainly to save labor or to cut down the cost of transporting fuel, a new problem of accountancy came into

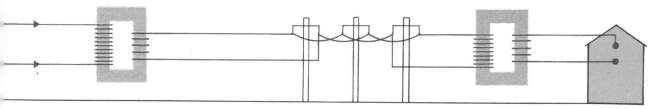

They step up voltage for overhead transmission, and reduce it for domestic use.

High-voltage cables carry current away from a power station for distribution.

the picture. Let us look first at how we make power available over a long distance.

The German mathematician Karl Gauss suggested that the double track of the railroad could convey the current without expenditure on wire or wiring. This did not work because a current carried at high voltage leaks across the moist wood supports and through the earth below. Another German, Karl Steinheil, found that the current will complete its circuit in one direction if we use the earth in place of a second wire. All we need do is sink deep metal plates connected with one terminal of the dynamo at one end and with one terminal of our electrical device at the other.

The 420-ton transformer at High Marnham power station, Nottinghamshire, the end of Britain's first 400,000-volt transmission line. It steps the 400,000-volt current down to 275,000 volts, for distribution to regional substations.

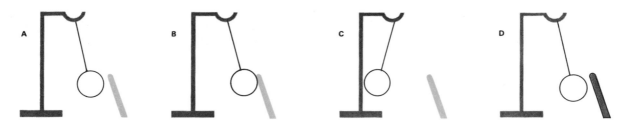

(A) A glass rod, rubbed with silk, carrying a positive charge, attracts a gold-covered pith ball. (B) When they touch, ball gives up its negative charge to rod. Ball now carries positive charge. (C) A positively charged glass rod now repels the ball. (D) Sealing wax rubbed with silk, carrying negative charge, attracts it.

Greater economy is possible when we understand how to make the best use of the metal wire the current flows through in the remainder of the circuit. Since the power in a circuit is the product of current and voltage, we can decrease the current and raise the voltage, or increase the current and lower the voltage, and still have the same power.

For a fixed output of 10,000 watts we may convey a current of 10 amps at 1000 volts, or 1000 amps at 10 volts. We know that current= voltage÷resistance $(C=V÷R)$. If we prefer the first alternative, the resistance needed is 100 ohms $(10=1000÷100)$. If we prefer the second alternative, the resistance needed is 0·01 ohm $(1000=10÷0·01)$. Now, the resistance of a wire made of a particular metal and of a fixed length depends on its thickness. The rule is that resistance is inversely proportional to the square of thickness. This means that if a copper wire $\frac{1}{100}$ in. thick offers a resistance of 100 ohms, we shall need an equally long copper wire 1 in. thick to give a resistance of 0·01 ohm. To maintain power transmission of 10,000 watts at 10 volts we need a hundred times as much metal as we do to maintain the same transmission at 1000 volts.

So at the power station we use a transformer☞ to step up the voltage enormously. We can then use much thinner, and therefore less expensive, wires to carry the current to where it is needed. In a dynamo generating direct current, high voltage causes sparking across the commutator and wears it out. If we want to use as little wire as need be, we shall therefore prefer to use an AC generator. This is why most power stations now generate alternating current, for which no commutator is needed.

Investigators gave the name *insulators* to substances, such as paper, that stick to the charged bodies that attract them. Other substances, such as gold leaf, which move toward the attracting body, but fly away upon touching it, they called *conductors*.

How bodies of either sort attract depends on what you rub them with. In stages 4 and 5 of our diagram above, glass rubbed with silk repels and sealing wax rubbed with fur attracts a pith ball covered with gold leaf. Clearly there are two kinds of charge. Benjamin Franklin called them *positive* and *negative*. These labels are useful to recall a simple rule: bodies with like charges repel each other; those with unlike charges attract each other.

People called "electrical" any device that recreated a miniature thunderstorm, before they knew that discharge of a Leyden jar and current from a voltaic battery are alike in other ways.

On the face of it, this is not obvious. A single cell produces *magnetic* effects and *chemical* effects (decomposition); but it is not easy to show that it can produce attractions, since you cannot pick up bits of paper with the two wires from the terminals. On the other hand, a frictional machine generates powerful *attractive* force; but its inventors had never been able to show that it produces magnetic or chemical effects.

Faraday settled the issue once for all. With a very sensitive gold-leaf detector (electroscope) he showed that a powerful voltaic battery can produce attractions and repulsions. By allowing sufficient time for the current of a frictional machine to discharge through a very high resistance, he was able to produce a magnetic effect, the deflection of a compass needle. By the slow discharge through a high resistance of a condenser fed by a frictional machine, he succeeded in producing the same chemical change that he was able to produce with a voltaic battery: his blue litmus paper turned red.

Generators of both sorts can do all the same jobs, but one of these jobs does not depend on flow of current. A current flows where there is a transfer of charge; but attractive force can exist without a flow of current. The parable of flowing water does not help us to understand why this should be so.

The gold-leaf electroscope can help us to do so, if we think of the plus and minus signs in the diagram on p. 51 as tiny pith balls of matter, the minus ones free to move. When the negatively charged glass rod is brought near the knob of the electroscope, it repels the negative particles in the knob, forcing them down into the gold leaves, which therefore repel one another. If we next take the glass rod away, the negative balls redistribute themselves in the knob as well as in the leaves; the whole apparatus is again neutral, and the leaves hang limply down. If we touch the lower part of the stem near the leaves *before* removing the glass rod, some of our imaginary negatively charged pith balls escape to the earth. When we take away the glass rod we therefore leave the electroscope with a positive charge, *opposite* to that of the glass rod. The leaves now retain the same sign and repel one another.

This process is known as charging by induction. The water-current parable makes no sense of it; but it does make sense when we begin to think of substances as collections of tiny bits, each with a charge of one sort or the other.

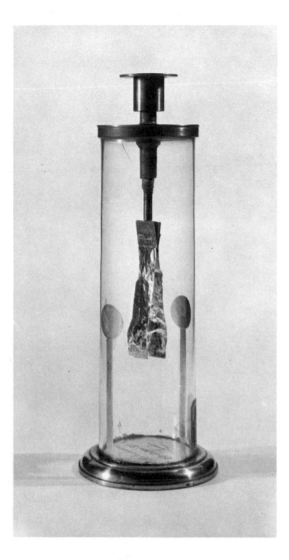

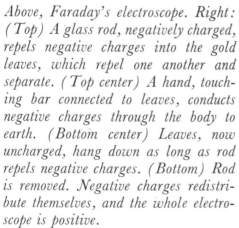

Above, Faraday's electroscope. Right: (Top) A glass rod, negatively charged, repels negative charges into the gold leaves, which repel one another and separate. (Top center) A hand, touching bar connected to leaves, conducts negative charges through the body to earth. (Bottom center) Leaves, now uncharged, hang down as long as rod repels negative charges. (Bottom) Rod is removed. Negative charges redistribute themselves, and the whole electroscope is positive.

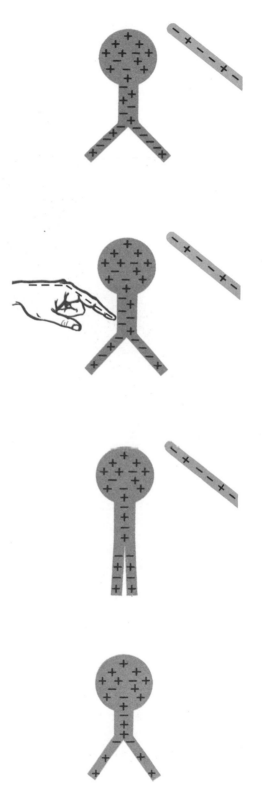

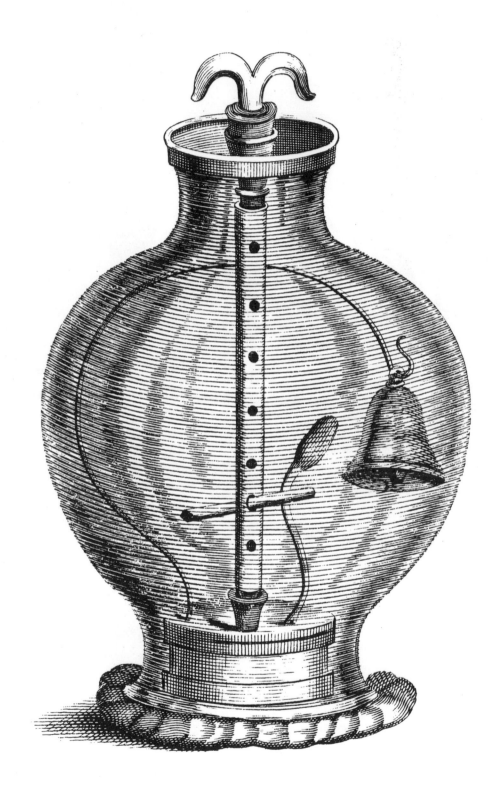

5 Alliance with Atoms

As early as the fifth century B.C., Greek philosophers had debated whether matter is as compact as it seems to be. Democritus, Epicurus, and others who believed that air has weight made the daring suggestion that all matter consists of tiny particles more or less loosely packed in the empty space of the vacuum. In their view, the blade that cuts a piece of solid matter or swishes through the air does not cut the particles. It merely brushes them aside. The word *atom*☞, which comes from Greek, means *uncuttable*.

Few people took the proposal seriously before Torricelli☞ showed how to make a vacuum. Shortly after his discovery, Pierre Gassendi, a French priest, wrote a treatise on these early Greek speculations. By then, the notion that matter is as compact as it seems was difficult to square with newly gained knowledge about the air and other gases.

With instruments available before the time of Galileo, there was little to suggest that matter is compressible; but such inventions as the air pump and the thermometer showed that we can change the volume that a fixed mass☞ occupies by changing the pressure or by applying heat.

About the mid-17th century, Robert Boyle☞ and Robert Hooke studied the effect of *pressure* on the volume of air. At the same temperature the rule is simple. By doubling the pressure, we halve the volume. By halving the pressure, we double the volume. If we mean by matter, that which has mass, the amount of matter remains the same when we double or halve the space to contain it. A century later, the Frenchman Jacques Charles discovered the rule that connects volume or pressure with *temperature*. If a gas is free to expand, its volume increases by equal steps for each degree; but its mass still remains the same.

Such facts encourage us to picture matter itself in either of two ways: as a sponge or as a puff of soot particles. Since we can crush a sponge or pack the particles of a cloud of soot into a smaller space, either parable fits the fact that bodies are compressible and expand when heated.

Boyle's vacuum glass for testing the effect of decreasing air pressure on sound.

Boyle showed that the air in a balloon expands as the pressure outside decreases.

When we deal with mixtures and compounds, it is easier to picture a mix-up of two sorts of particles than to picture how two sponges can interlock. Hooke and Boyle preferred to liken a gas to a cloud of particles, because they were able to show that air consists of two kinds of matter. It is, in fact, largely a mixture of two gases, nitrogen and oxygen.

In their time it was difficult to convince people that there are very many kinds of "air," as they then called gases. Chemists did not yet distinguish between mere mixtures, such as a syrup of sugar and water, and compounds built up in fixed proportions by weight from the simpler substances we now call elements. Atoms had little interest for the practical man until chemists discovered more about compounds.

By the end of the 18th century, chemists had discovered many different gases. They had labeled as elements☞ those they could not break down—oxygen, nitrogen, and hydrogen. They had labeled as compounds those they could build up by combining other substances in fixed proportion by weight, for instance ammonia and nitrous oxide. They also recognized as elements the liquid mercury and the solids carbon, sulfur, phosphorus, gold, silver, copper, tin, lead, and zinc.

They found that when elements combine to form compounds they do so in certain fixed ratios by weight, and in these fixed ratios simple multiples of the same numbers turn up again and again. For instance, ammonia consists of nitrogen and hydrogen in the ratio 14:3, nitrous oxide of nitrogen and oxygen in the ratio 14:8, water of hydrogen and oxygen in the ratio 1:8. This rule holds good equally for the smallest and largest measurable quantities; and the sponge model does not help us to understand why it should. In 1808, when John Dalton of Manchester revived the atomic view of Hooke and Boyle, chemists had good reason to respond favorably. If we can picture the smallest quantity of ammonia as a cluster of a definite number of hydrogen atoms, each with the same mass, and a definite number of nitrogen atoms, each with the same mass, piling up larger quantities from the smallest possible quantity of the gas will not change the ratio of nitrogen to hydrogen by weight.

Our picture of such an atom cluster must take into account the fact that each gaseous element has its own characteristic density. For instance, nitrogen weighs 14 times as much as the same volume of hydrogen at the same temperature and pressure. If we say that the particles of nitrogen and the particles of hydrogen are of equal mass, the same volume of nitrogen must contain 14 times as many particles as the hydrogen; but if we say that the nitrogen particle is 14 times as heavy as the hydrogen particle, equal volumes of the two gases at the same temperature and pressure must contain equal numbers of particles.

If we like to think of such particles as the smallest quantity of matter, we must turn down the first view. The space that a single hydrogen particle could fill would then be the smallest possible space; the number of particles of nitrogen contained within this smallest possible space would be 14 and the smallest quantity of nitrogen would therefore be 14 particles. Besides, our first view does not suggest any clue to why nitrogen and hydrogen differ in so many ways other than weight.

If we therefore plump for the second view, we have to ask whether the particles of an element exist as single atoms or clusters of atoms, like the particles of a compound, now called molecules. A French chemist discovered a master clue. Louis Gay-Lussac showed that when gaseous elements combine to form compounds they do so in simple numerical ratios by volume.

At a temperature of 100°C and at atmospheric pressure, 200 volumes of hydrogen combine with 100 volumes of oxygen to make 200 volumes of steam; 200 volumes of nitrogen combine with 100 volumes of oxygen to make 200 volumes of nitrous oxide.

If equal volumes contain equal numbers of particles, 1 particle of oxygen must go into the making of 2 molecules of steam; and 1 particle of oxygen must go into the making of 2 molecules of nitrous oxide. So the oxygen particles must contain 2, or some even number of, atoms. The study of other combinations leads to the same conclusion with reference to hydrogen, nitrogen, and chlorine.

In 1811 Amedeo Avogadro☞, an Italian chemist, therefore sharpened the outline of the particle theory by proposing that equal volumes of all gases at the same temperature and pressure contain the same number of *molecules*. If the molecules of hydrogen, nitrogen, oxygen, and chlorine all contain even numbers of atoms, it is simplest to guess that they contain 2. If so, masses of their atoms are in the same ratio as their densities at the same pressure and temperature. When we know this, we can work out how the weight of an atom of any gaseous element compares with the weight of an atom of hydrogen. If we call the weight of hydrogen 1, that of nitrogen is 14, that of oxygen 16, that of chlorine 35.5. We now call these numbers the atomic weights☞ of the elements.

The simplest guess turns out to give us a satisfactory system of bookkeeping as well as a satisfactory shorthand for chemical compounds. When we label ammonia gas as NH_3 we mean that it is formed by combining 1 atom of nitrogen (N) with 3 atoms of hydrogen (H). Knowing these proportions as well as the atomic weights of nitrogen and hydrogen, we can calculate that 14 grams of nitrogen combine with 3 grams of hydrogen to make 17 grams of ammonia gas.

Three clues encourage us to think of matter as a cloud of particles. One—heat expands gases and pressure packs them into a smaller space. Two—the pith ball model helps us to picture electrical attraction. A third clue comes from how electric current breaks down chemical compounds.

It is important to know that chemically pure water does not conduct an electric current. If we add a trace of table salt it does, but if we

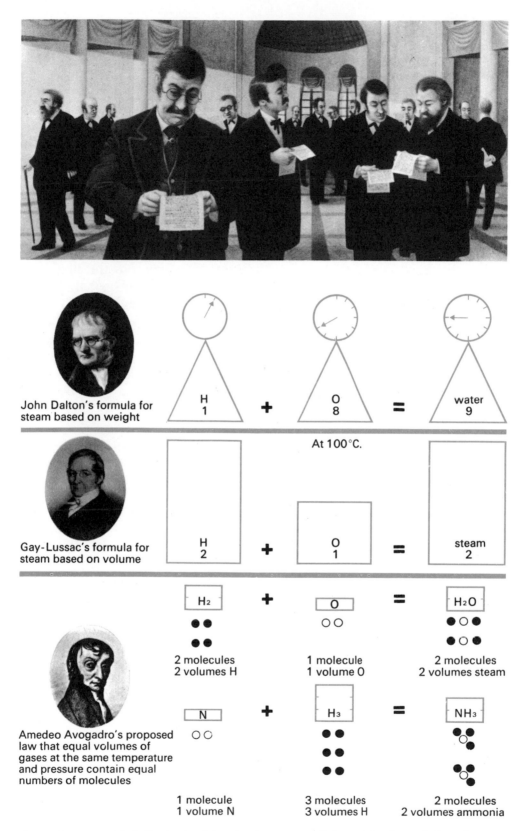

John Dalton's formula for steam based on weight

H 1 + O 8 = water 9

At 100°C.

Gay-Lussac's formula for steam based on volume

H 2 + O 1 = steam 2

Amedeo Avogadro's proposed law that equal volumes of gases at the same temperature and pressure contain equal numbers of molecules

H₂ + O = H₂O

2 molecules
2 volumes H

1 molecule
1 volume O

2 molecules
2 volumes steam

N + H₃ = NH₃

1 molecule
1 volume N

3 molecules
3 volumes H

2 molecules
2 volumes ammonia

Avogadro reconciled Dalton's formula for steam, HO, with that of Gay-Lussac, H₂O, based on volume. His proposal finally won recognition in 1860, when it was put before the first International Chemists' Convention (top of page).

add sugar it does not. All substances that make water conduct, such as metallic salts, break down, as in the process of electroplating. In doing so they decompose the water itself. We call them *electrolytes*.

Our pith ball model makes us think of a current as a stream of charged particles. If so, electrolytes must be substances with molecules that break down when dissolved in water into positively charged fragments attracted to the negative terminal (*cathode*) and negatively charged ones attracted to the positive terminal (*anode*).

Faraday discovered that when the same current releases two different elements by decomposition, the masses released depend on their atomic weights. When the same current frees silver in one vessel and hydrogen in another, the mass of silver released is 108 times as great as that of hydrogen, as is true of their atomic weights. This fits into the picture if we say that the acidulated water contains positively charged hydrogen atoms and that the silver-salt solution contains positively charged silver atoms. The ratio of the masses set free then means that the number of atoms that go to the cathode in each vessel is the same for equal current in equal time.

We can now picture the strength of the current as the rate at which the cathode takes up positive, and the anode negative, charges. When the same current flows, the charged atoms (ions) of hydrogen thus carry the same positive charge as the ions of silver.

We can measure a water current by dividing the total amount of water that flows by the time it takes it to flow. We can measure an electric current (amperes☞) by dividing the total amount of charge by the time (seconds) the current flows. If current is charge divided by time, charge is current (amperes) multiplied by time (seconds).

The first fling produced by a momentary current in a very sluggish galvanometer depends only on charge in this sense. We can thus measure exactly how attractive force depends on charge, hence what charge keeps a droplet floating between charged plates. Such minute charges are always a multiple of one number, which we must regard as the smallest possible charge. Let us call it e.

Faraday's picture of how solutions conduct gives us a way of measuring the actual mass of an atom. Suppose that a current of $\frac{1}{10}$ ampere flows 1000 seconds, decomposing water. Since charge is current multiplied by time, the charge in our example is $\frac{1}{10}$ multiplied by 1000, or 100 ampere-seconds. If our total charge is 100, then, and we call the single smallest quantity of charge e, we can find the *number* of single charges by dividing the total charge (100) by the quantity of the smallest charge (e). Since each hydrogen atom carries only one charge, this number ($\frac{100}{e}$) is also the number of hydrogen atoms set free by our current in 1000 seconds. We can easily measure the total mass of hydrogen collected in the glass cylinder over the cathode; and since we know the number ($\frac{100}{e}$) of hydrogen atoms contained in this total mass, we can calculate the mass of one single hydrogen atom.

Other lines of attack led to the same figure when physicists studied how gases can conduct a current. Meanwhile, chemists had hit on a new way of detecting elements in very minute quantities.

We all know that a pinch of salt (a sodium compound) burns with a bright yellow light in a barely visible blue flame. Any element intensifies the color of the flame in some region of the spectrum. We can thus recognize its presence in minute quantities by means of the spectroscope.

We call the bright regions that the spectroscope shows up when an element is incandescent its "flame spectrum." That of a compound shows merely the same regions as the elements in its molecule. So the flame spectrum tells us what atoms are present in it.

In 1740, the French priest Jean Nollet, who did much to perfect the condenser for use with the older frictional generators, made one very novel observation. He allowed an electrical machine to discharge through a vessel connected with an air pump, and found that a succession of separate sparks then gives place to a continuous glow, as in a neon tube, when pressure is reduced. There was no further advance toward understanding the spark discharge until Faraday took up the

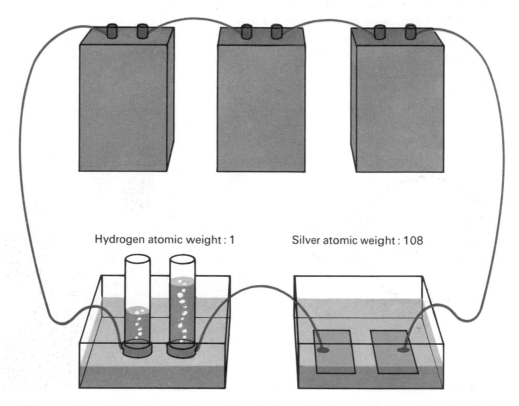

Hydrogen atomic weight : 1   Silver atomic weight : 108

The atomic weight of silver is 108, and that of hydrogen 1. Faraday found that when the same current frees silver in one vessel and hydrogen in another vessel, the mass of silver deposited is 108 times greater than that of hydrogen.

problem where Nollet had left it. By 1850 physicists knew more precisely how air at low pressure can conduct a current at sufficiently high voltage. In 1858 a German scientific worker named Julius Plucker noticed that the continuous visible beam in a low-pressure tube wobbles sideways when a magnet comes near it.

Seemingly, water conducts a current because its molecules break down into the positively and negatively charged atoms or atom-clusters now called *ions*. Physicists began to suspect that something similar happens during the spark discharge when other experimenters showed that a positively charged plate will deflect the glow in the low-pressure discharge tube. The direction in which the magnet deflects the glow and the effect of a nearby charged plate on it both suggest that the visible beam is produced by a stream of swiftly moving negative particles heating the air in its wake to incandescence.

When this view was gaining ground, Wilhelm von Röntgen noticed that some chemicals will fluoresce (glow in the dark) in the neighborhood of the low-pressure tube. He also discovered that a photographic plate well wrapped in cardboard blurs when brought near it. He labeled whatever escapes from the tube as X rays☞ and showed that these could not be a stream of charged particles, because a magnet or charged plate has no effect on their direction. Such X rays pass as easily through flesh as through cardboard but less easily through bone. Their discovery therefore had great value for the surgeon.

Henri Becquerel, a professor in Paris, found that salts of the rare heavy metals thorium and uranium reproduce both effects of the X rays. The

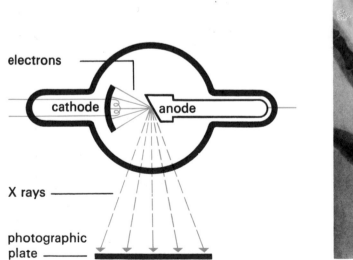

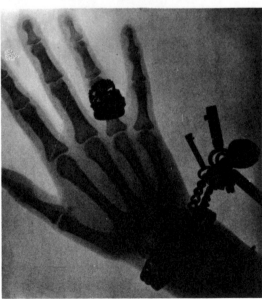

Left, X rays are produced when a stream of electrons passes at high speed from the cathode to the anode in a vacuum tube. Right, an X-ray photograph of 1896. Opposite, using X rays to check the quality of new turbine blades.

same substances fluoresce in their neighborhood, and a photographic plate fully protected from ordinary light blurs near them. He suggested to his pupil Marie Curie that she should search for minerals containing these radioactive metals.

One such mineral, called pitchblende, contains an appreciable amount of uranium and is very radioactive. Marie Curie analyzed how much uranium it contains and found that the amount was not sufficient to account for such intense fluorescence or reaction from a photographic plate. So she deduced that some other constituent must be present in pitchblende to account for the excessive radioactivity☞ of the mineral, and she set about concentrating it.

The outcome was the isolation in 1898 of a new element☞, radium, much more active than thorium or uranium. It had an as yet undetected property that uranium and thorium also have. Its salts give out heat spontaneously without decomposing to an extent detectable by ordinary chemical tests.

Many scientists, including especially Ernest Rutherford☞ and Frederick Soddy, were eager to study its peculiarities. By screening the invisible beam that comes out of a lead tube containing some radium salt at the closed end, and by letting it pass near a magnet or a charged plate, they were able to dissect it into three parts: positively charged particles called *alpha rays*; negative particles (electrons☞) as in the low-pressure tube; and highly penetrating rays like those Röntgen discovered. Physicists call the last *gamma rays* and the stream of electrons *beta rays*.

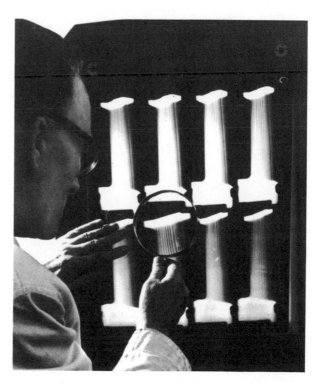

On trapping the alpha rays, they observed that the air showed the spectrum of the light, inert sun-element, helium. This suggested that alpha particles are positively charged atoms of helium. If so, the heavy radium atom itself is in a constant state of extremely slow disintegration with accompanying release of heat. Hitherto man's only source of heat—other than the sun, the hot spring, or the volcano—had been what he could tap when molecules break down and atoms combine to form new molecules. Man had stumbled on a new store of power.

If we measure the bending of the cathode stream of negatively charged particles both in a magnetic and in an electric field, it is possible to calculate the mass and the charge of the particles directly. Joseph Thomson did so in the 1890s. The charge is the already known smallest unit, e ampere-seconds. The mass turns out to be tiny—about $\frac{1}{2000}$ that of the hydrogen atom.

In the cathode tube we get a stream of particles from the negative terminal causing a glow opposite that terminal. We can construct a low-pressure tube in such a way that we get a glow opposite the *positive* terminal. A charged plate and a magnet will each deflect this glow as if it were due to the impact of positively charged particles (ions).

If the gas in the tube is hydrogen, the mass of these particles, called *protons*☞, is almost exactly the same as that of an atom of hydrogen. The charge on the hydrogen ion (proton) is equal and opposite to the electron charge. Thus hydrogen conducts when its molecules break down into free electrons and atoms that have lost one electron.

Rutherford, who first bent the beam given off by radium in electric and magnetic fields, found that its beta ray is a stream of electrons and its alpha ray is a stream of positive particles each four times as heavy as the hydrogen atom. Since 4 is the atomic weight of helium, this tells the same story as the spectroscope. Rutherford also found that the charge on the alpha particle is equal and opposite to the charge on two electrons.

If alpha particles bombard a screen of gold leaf in front of a plate coated with a substance that will fluoresce under their impact, Rutherford found that most of the particles shoot straight through the screen. Some scatter, as if repelled sideways by the gold atoms. Others turn back, as if by collision.

Seemingly, therefore, atoms of heavy solids lie far apart like stars in empty space. Each electron must also lie far from the positively charged core, as the moon is far from the earth. From now on, physicists began to picture every atom as a minute solar system in which the positively charged core corresponds to the sun, and electrons to the planets revolving in orbits around it. Since radium atoms shoot off alpha particles as the sun perhaps shot off the planets, it seemed that the core itself might be breakable.

At this stage, physicists knew that the core, now called the nucleus, of the helium atom is four times as heavy as a hydrogen atom, and that it lacks two electrons present in the neutral helium atom. If the hydrogen atom is like a planet with one tiny moon, the helium atom is like a planet four times as large with two tiny moons.

It was therefore tempting to picture the helium nucleus as a cluster of two protons and two equally heavy neutral particles. If all atoms consist of protons and such neutral particles, the atomic weights of all elements must be whole numbers. Fifty years ago this did not square with what chemists had found out. Just before the outbreak of World War I, newly discovered facts forced chemists to revise their views about what they had so far called elements.

When gases diffuse through a porous membrane they do so at a speed that depends on their density. It is therefore possible to separate a lighter gas from a heavier one by repeated diffusion. If we treat a

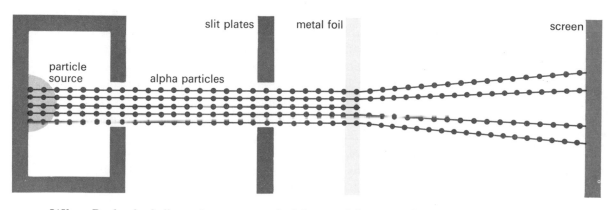

When Rutherford directed a stream of alpha particles at a sheet of gold leaf, he found that most of them passed through, but a few bounced back to source.

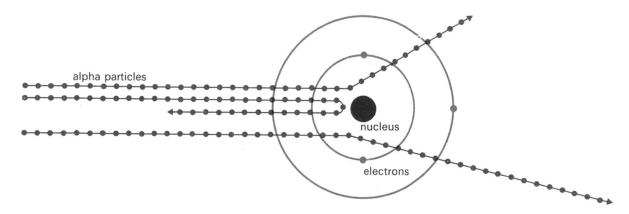

Rutherford realized that the alpha particles that were rebounding had collided with the core of an atom—and that the atom consisted of a heavy, positively charged nucleus around which orbited light, negatively charged electrons.

gaseous element in this way, we find that it is in fact a mixture of substances with exactly the same chemical properties, but with different atomic weights. Ordinary oxygen is a mixture of two such *isotopes*☞, as we now call them. The atomic weight of the lighter is 16, that of the other (and rarer) 17.

Though the atomic weights of elements as known at the beginning of the century are not whole numbers, those of isotopes are. Thus the mass of the atom of an isotope is an exact multiple of the mass of the hydrogen atom. The nuclei of isotopes of the same element have the same charge, corresponding to a fixed number of protons. So we may suppose that such isotopes differ only because they contain one or more neutral ingredients whose mass is almost the same as that of the hydrogen atom.

The positive charge of the nucleus is equivalent to the number of electrons in the neutral atom. We call this the *atomic number*☞ of an element. Isotopes of the same element thus have the same atomic number. The atomic number identifies the characteristic chemical properties of an element.

The discovery of isotopes encouraged the hope that it might be possible to break down the nucleus of the atoms of elements other than hydrogen. Rutherford hit on the idea of using the swiftly moving helium ions of the alpha beam from radium as missiles. In 1919 he found that their passage through nitrogen will occasionally cause scintillations on a screen six times beyond the normal range of an alpha particle. Rutherford discovered that the particles that hit the screen carried a positive charge, as shown by magnetic deflection.

Further study of the track of the helium ion through a cloud chamber showed that it occasionally forks. Two tracks then appear, one more oblique and of shorter range than the other. Rutherford was able to calculate that such tracks correspond to the flight of a hydrogen atom or proton and of a heavy oxygen atom. The arithmetic of atomic weights and positive charges (atomic numbers) involved agrees with this calculation, as our diagram shows.

In 1932 John Cockcroft☞ and Ernest Walton used protons to bombard the light metal lithium, and produced particles recognized as helium by their spectrum. If we assume that the lithium and hydrogen nuclei unite to form two helium nuclei the figures balance. These and other experiments strengthened the belief that the nucleus of atoms heavier than hydrogen consists of protons (hydrogen nuclei) and of neutral particles (neutrons) of equivalent mass.

The first clue to the proof of the neutron's existence came in 1930 when Walther Bothe and H. Becker in Germany produced a new type of very penetrating ray by letting the radium beam play on the light metal beryllium. These rays produce effects like those of gamma rays.

In France Frédéric Joliot and his wife Irène Curie, and in England James Chadwick, showed that they are streams of uncharged particles. Their tracks in a cloud chamber indicate collisions with nuclei as in Rutherford's experiments.

An explanation that fits the facts is that the helium ion (atomic number 2) from the radium beam unites with the nucleus of a beryllium atom (atomic number 4) to make the nucleus of an atom of carbon (atomic number 6). Here the arithmetic of the atomic numbers corresponding to positive charges balances: $2+4=6$; but the atomic weights of the nuclei involved do *not* balance. The helium ion (atomic weight 4)

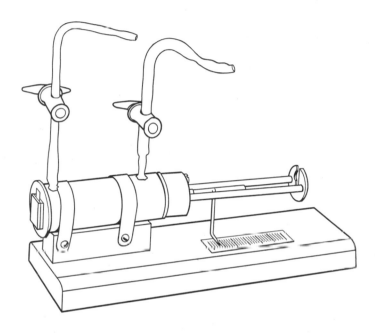

The apparatus Rutherford used to break down the nuclei of hydrogen atoms.

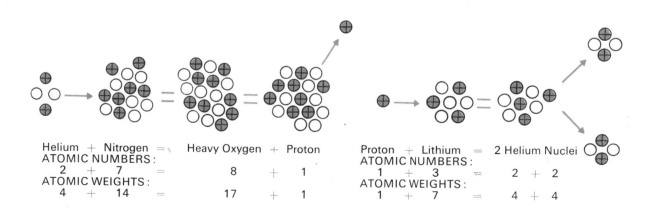

Helium	+	Nitrogen	=	Heavy Oxygen	+	Proton		Proton	+	Lithium	=	2 Helium Nuclei
ATOMIC NUMBERS:								ATOMIC NUMBERS:				
2	+	7	=	8	+	1		1	+	3	=	2 + 2
ATOMIC WEIGHTS:								ATOMIC WEIGHTS:				
4	+	14	=	17	+	1		1	+	7	=	4 + 4

Diagram showing the arithmetic of atomic weights and atomic numbers.

combines with the beryllium nucleus (atomic weight 9) to make a carbon nucleus (atomic weight 12). A neutral particle with the atomic weight of 1 is missing from the weight budget. Such neutrons, then, are the source of the new rays that Bothe and Becker discovered.

We have now seen that the nucleus accounts for nearly all the mass of the atom. The protons of the nucleus account for its net positive charge, and its mass depends on both protons and neutrons. The mass of each neutron is almost exactly the same as that of the proton. The atoms of the heaviest elements contain more neutrons than protons. Such are the elements that are more or less unstable—for instance, radium, one of the heaviest.

Having no charge, neutrons suffer no repulsion in the vicinity of a nucleus. They can collide head-on at top speed. Accordingly, the Italian physicist Fermi recognized that they are ideal missiles, easily manu-factured by the impact of alpha particles on beryllium, boron, and other light elements.

In 1938, Otto Hahn and Fritz Strassmann in Germany showed that the atom of uranium breaks down under the impact of neutron bom-bardment into fragments of roughly equal size. The daughter nuclei fly apart at great speed. It seemed very likely that in the breakdown free neutrons would be released, which would in turn hit other nuclei and repeat the process *ad infinitum.*

At the beginning of our own century, physicists who measured the detectable heat production in the minutely slow disintegration of radium had already calculated that its complete breakdown to its end products (lead and helium) would set free more than a quarter of a million times as much heat as is liberated by the same quantity of coal.

Hence if we can start a chain reaction in which neutrons break up uranium atoms into fragments with liberation of more neutrons to do the same thing repeatedly, it should have stupendous explosive power. In 1939, physicists of all the warring nations concentrated on finding a recipe.

At the outset, they knew that the empty space between atoms is relatively vast. Hence the chance that any neutron used as a missile will collide head on with a nucleus when it strikes a small piece of uranium is extremely remote. Unless the bulk of uranium is large enough, no chain reaction will occur. The major problem was to dis-cover what bulk is large enough. If, when we know the answer, our only aim is to make an explosion, we can do so by bringing together two previously insulated blocks, totaling more than half this critical bulk. Then the chain reaction begins and grows.

This briefly is the principle of the first atomic bomb, exploded at the Alamogordo Air Base in New Mexico in the southwest United States on July 16, 1945. The bomb was lashed to a steel tower in the desert.

The explosive power of 100 lb of the uranium isotope 235 may be equivalent to that of 20,000 tons of nitrates. Top, Bikini after the explosion of the atom bomb in 1946. Lower, an underwater explosion of nitrates off British Columbia.

Ten miles away observers watched. Just before dawn the bomb was set off. A tremendous burst of light threw golden, purple, violet, gray, and blue searchlights over the whole country, outlining nearby mountains with a light far stronger than the noonday sun. A few seconds later, came a tornado-like air blast accompanied by a sustained roar, as of a continuing explosion. A many-colored cloud rose 40,000 feet into the air. The heat of the explosion has been estimated at several million degrees. It vaporized the steel tower and fused sand in a huge crater into glass. One month later the atomic bomb's horrifying performance in two cities of Japan brought the war to an end.

Just as the fission (splitting) of a heavy atom such as that of uranium or thorium liberates a vast store of heat, so does the union (fusion) of two light atoms such as lithium and hydrogen to form two atoms of helium. At very high temperatures such as the atomic bomb generates, this type of reaction—the source of the sun's heat—takes place. Such is the principle of the hydrogen bomb whose explosive power has threatened universal destruction since the first was exploded in 1954.

In making a fission bomb the problem is to produce a single concentrated uncontrolled chain reaction. In learning to use atomic fission for other, peaceful, purposes the problem was to produce a steady, controlled chain reaction of predictable power that could be harnessed, and to be able to slow down the reaction when it becomes too intense. Happily, research that made it possible to exploit the destructive power of the atom also pointed the way to the more difficult problem of releasing its vast store of energy at a rate slow enough for doing useful work. Indeed, this had been accomplished by those who made the first bomb; for they could not have carried out the necessary experiments without first learning how to control a chain reaction.

The possibility of controlling nuclear fission depends primarily on the fact that some substances, such as graphite, slow down the speed of neutrons, and that others, such as cadmium, capture neutrons and prevent their bombarding the nuclei of nearby atoms. In the first large-scale chain-reaction tests, made in 1941, a "pile" of graphite bricks was built to separate small lumps of uranium. The core of the complex reactors of today still uses graphite, as a casing into which movable sticks of uranium are inserted until the total mass of uranium inside the reactor reaches critical size. Control rods—e.g. of cadmium—control the rate of chain reaction.

Tremendous heat is created by the splitting of the nuclei of the atoms of uranium, thorium, or other fissionable material, including man-made isotopes of these two elements. This heat is transferred to a conventional boiler by a coolant—gas or water—which absorbs heat from the reactor and in effect cools it. In the boiler, steam is produced and directed to a turbine where it performs work.

Research in many countries has improved the efficiency of atomic engines and in the next few decades atomic power may become the main electricity producer. But the release of atomic power has brought with it many other uses, in scientific research, in manufacturing processes, and in farming.

Knowledge of the atomic nature of matter has influenced all fields of science more and more during the past 60 years. Only during the last 50 years has atomic research made a material contribution to everyday life. One important use of atomic engines to date is the production of radioisotopes. A radioisotope of an element is chemically like other isotopes of that element, but less stable and consequently in a constant state of disintegration. The first artificial radioisotope was produced by the Joliot-Curies. They bombarded aluminum (13 protons, 14 neutrons, atomic weight 27) with alpha particles and created a substance whose nucleus contained 15 protons and 15 neutrons, weighing 30. A substance with 15 protons should be phosphorus; but phosphorus has 16 neutrons and an atomic weight of 31. The Joliot-Curies found that chemically the new substance actually was phosphorus. They had artificially produced a new isotope of phosphorus; and, more important, they found it to be radioactive.

Scientists have since produced radioactive isotopes of a large number of known elements. Some retain radioactivity for thousands of years, others for only fractions of a second. They have all the properties of natural radioactive substances, which are comparatively rare; and they are far less expensive. The length of time a substance retains its radioactivity is measured in terms of its half-life. For instance, half of any amount of radium (half-life some 1600 years) disappears in 1600 years, giving off atomic particles all the time. In the next 1600 years half of what is left disappears, and so on.

Because they are constantly giving off subatomic particles, radioisotopes announce their presence wherever they are and can easily be detected. Such isotopes can therefore be used as tracers by adding them to whatever we wish to trace. Detection of tracers is made either photographically or by an electrical detector such as the Geiger counter. For instance, the biologist can use them in the study of plant and animal growth.

Further, the radiation from radioisotopes duplicates the gamma-ray radiation of radium and can therefore be used as a radium substitute. In Franklin's day, mankind stood on the threshold of the age of steam; in Lincoln's day, on the threshold of the age of electrical power; before the death of F. D. Roosevelt, on the threshold of the atomic age. Today one or other source of power is dramatically changing the face of lands where the muscular effort of man or beast has hitherto been almost the only means of doing work.

But although atomic power has become economical, we need not suppose it will be the answer to power problems everywhere. Some highly industrialized countries where water power is now the major source of electricity☞ are using only a small percentage of their total resources. Nuclear reactors☞ would have to be much cheaper before such countries would find it worthwhile to buy them. But the realization of atomic power seems to have freed men's minds from hidebound thinking; and many novel projects are afoot in the world of today.

Water power is an ever-increasing source of electricity production, and engineering know-how is extending its use in many ways. In many places more mechanization is the only guarantee of better health and comfort, especially in countries where the standard of life is poor. For such, the prospect of prosperity depends on the best use of locally available power. The thriving bauxite industry in Mackenzie, on the Demerara River in Guyana, illustrates this. The country has vast deposits of bauxite, the main ore of aluminum, but the cost either of carrying the ore out of the jungle or of carrying supplies of fuel into the jungle to process it was prohibitive. Today a hydroelectric power station on the Demerara River offloads on a worldwide market a large new supply of the metal.

Nuclear submarines like the Thomas Edison *can travel underwater for long periods, because their engines, unlike diesels, need no air. Some are equipped as mobile missile bases; others specialize in locating and tracking down ships.*

Hydroelectric schemes often tie up with other community projects, such as flood control and irrigation. The same construction that can supply a large area with electric power can help to prevent disastrous periodic floods and also to make large new areas of land available for agriculture.

Much of the new power man is learning to make better use of is less due to new theoretical discoveries than to progress in engineering: the production of materials to withstand great water pressure; the production of machines to perform gigantic tasks that no army of workers, however vast, could do well enough or fast enough.

Engineers are also making better use of local resources of natural power to do jobs for which we have mainly relied on electricity during the past century. We are learning to make more use of hot springs and the heat of the earth's crust. In tropical countries, architects are designing buildings that use the heat of the sun to create air currents for ventilation. Engineers and designers are also trying out ways of using the heat of the sun, the wind, volcanoes, and tides to produce electricity.

Whether produced by coal, oil, water, or by splitting atoms, electricity is the great servant of mankind. It allows the inexpensive and efficient transmission of power from one place to another. Coal, at one

The water pool at Dresden nuclear power station, Illinois. In the reactor below it, water is heated to boiling point by atomic fission. The steam is used to generate electricity; it travels directly from the reactor to the turbine.

time the major source of electric power, is getting more expensive yearly. Large populations and large industrial demands have long been using up the top layers of coal; and the ever-deepening seams are more difficult and more costly to mine. For this reason alone, water power is fast becoming the source of electricity wherever it is available.

Growing demands for electricity, especially where little water power is available, encourage engineers to experiment with ways of using power sources other than oil, coal, and falling water. In the last resort almost all power is solar power. We use the sun's energy stored in coal and oil and wood when we burn them, and the sun's heat is what distributes the water over dry land. Winds blow largely because the sun makes one part of the earth warmer than another; and life itself would not exist on our planet if there were no sun. In recent years, as the diagram opposite shows there has been real progress toward economical use of solar energy directly to drive the blades of a turbine☞; success

The turbo-generators that produce electricity at Larderello power station, Italy, are driven by natural steam that gushes from especially-drilled wells.

might bring otherwise unforeseeable prosperity to tropical countries. Two other sources of natural heat, volcanoes and the temperature difference between different water levels, can be tapped to produce electricity. Improvements in the design of propellers have given rise to a new interest in windmills for generating power. And a bold French project is now harnessing the great tides of the Rance estuary in the world's first tidal power station.

Such new efforts to produce electricity give evidence of the increasing need for power to feed, to clothe, and to house the world's growing populations, now demanding freedom from agelong slavery to the single problem of keeping alive. Power can never create a better world. But only power can create the conditions in which a better world will be possible. Power can give man the time and many of the tools, though not the inclination, to indulge in some of the more beautiful efforts he is capable of making.

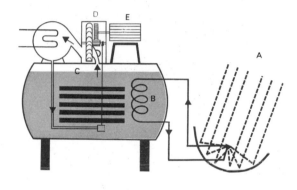

A solar generator, left, uses the sun's rays (A) to heat fluid circulating through tube (B). In tank (C), the fluid vaporizes under pressure to drive a turbine (D) that turns the electric generator (E). Below, an experimental windmill. Diagram, below left, shows how its hollow propeller throws air out by centrifugal force from tips of blades, so that the inrush of air at foot will drive a turbine.

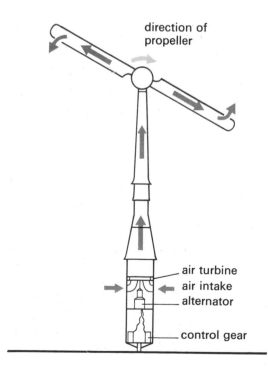

direction of propeller

air turbine
air intake
alternator

control gear

Glossary

In this Glossary, as in the rest of the book, the symbol☞ means that the term it follows has its own alphabetical entry in the Glossary, to which you may refer for a fuller definition or for more information.

AC (ALTERNATING CURRENT) A flow of electricity that rises to a maximum in one direction, then decreases to zero, then reverses itself, rising to a maximum in the opposite direction . . . and so on. The number of such cycles per second (cps) is the *frequency* of alternation.

ACCELERATION The rate of change of velocity☞, measured as change in velocity (e.g. feet per second) in unit time (e.g. per second). It is expressed as feet per second per second (ft/sec²).

AERODYNAMICS The branch of dynamics that deals with the motion of air and other gases, and the forces acting upon bodies passing through them—especially aircraft, rockets, and missiles.

AMPERE A unit for measuring electric current, equal to the flow of one coulomb☞ per second.

ARCHIMEDES (about 287-212 B.C.) Greek mathematician and inventor, born in Syracuse, Sicily. Archimedes discovered the law of the lever (p. 9), and invented an instrument for raising water—a screw that revolved inside a tightly fitting cylinder. He also discovered the principle that a body plunged into fluid loses as much of its weight as will counterbalance the weight of the fluid it displaces.

ATOM The smallest part of an element that can take part in a chemical change. Every atom consists of a positively charged core, or *nucleus*, orbited by negatively charged *electrons*. The nucleus contains positively charged *protons* and neutral *neutrons* of almost equal mass. The mass of the electron is only $\frac{1}{1836}$th that of the proton, but its negative charge exactly balances the positive charge of the proton. Every atom contains an equal number of protons and electrons. So the atom is an electrically neutral system with most of its mass in the nucleus.

The number of protons and neutrons (called *nucleons*) in the nucleus determines the *mass number* of the atom. Different isotopes☞ have different mass numbers. For instance, the ordinary hydrogen nucleus has 1 proton, no neutron; its mass number is 1. The nucleus of the heavy hydrogen isotope deuterium has 1 proton and 1 neutron; its mass number is 2.

Archimedes (about 287-212 B.C.).

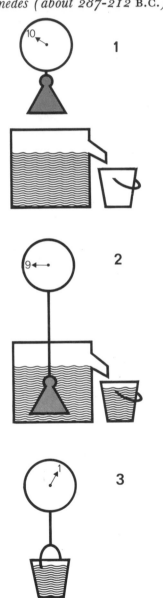

(1) Body weighs 10 lb. (2) Immersed in water, it weighs 9 lb. (3) The water it has displaced weighs 1 lb.

Radius of atom 1 km

Radius of nucleus 10 cm

Radius of electron 1 cm

Comparative dimensions of the atom, nucleus, and electron (magnified).

Robert Boyle (1627-91).

ATOMIC MASS UNIT (AMU) A unit of mass used for expressing the masses of different isotopes☞ of elements.

ATOMIC NUMBER The number of electrons rotating around the nucleus of an atom☞, or the number of protons in the nucleus.

ATOMIC WEIGHT The mean weight of the atoms of an element expressed in atomic mass units☞.

AVOGADRO, AMADEO (1776-1856) Italian physicist, born in Turin. He became professor of higher physics at Turin University and made a number of important discoveries about the nature of atoms☞ and molecules☞. These included the principle now known as *Avogadro's Law*: that equal volumes of different gases at the same temperature and pressure contain the same number of molecules.

BALLISTICS The branch of physics that deals with the motion, flight paths, and effects of projectiles☞, especially missile weapons.

BATTERY An array of wet or dry cells in which chemical energy is turned into electrical energy.

BOILING POINT The temperature at which a substance changes its state from liquid to gas. The boiling point of water is 100° C, 212° F.

BOYLE, ROBERT (1627-91) British physicist and chemist, born in Ireland. Boyle investigated the chemistry of combustion☞ and respiration; the properties of air (p. 55); the expansive force of freezing water; specific gravities; and the nature of electricity. His greatest contribution to physics was the formulation of *Boyle's Law*, which states that the volume of any gas, at a constant temperature, is inversely proportional to the pressure upon the gas.

BRITISH THERMAL UNIT (Btu) The quantity of heat needed to raise 1 lb of water through 1° F.

CALDER HALL The home, in Cumberland, England, of the first commercial power station operating on nuclear energy. It began production in 1956. See also NUCLEAR REACTOR.

CALORIE The quantity of heat needed to raise 1 gm of water from 14.5° C to 15.5° C. The kilogram-calorie, written Calorie, or Kcal, is equal to 1000 calories; this is the Calorie that dieticians use to measure the energy value of foods.

CENTIGRADE (or CELSIUS) SCALE A temperature scale that takes the melting point of ice as 0° C and the boiling point of water as 100° C. It is used by scientists throughout the world and usually where the metric system is used. To convert centigrade to Fahrenheit☞, multiply the reading by 9, divide by 5, and add 32.

CHAIN REACTION Any process of molecular or nuclear reaction in which one nuclear transformation triggers off a whole series.

COCKCROFT, SIR JOHN DOUGLAS (1897-1967) British physicist and co-winner, with Ernest Walton☞, of the Nobel Prize for physics, in 1951. The prize was awarded for their pioneer work in splitting the atom (p. 64).

COMBUSTION ("burning") The liberation of chemical energy☞, usually by oxidizing fuel molecules in atmospheric oxygen.

COMPOUND ENGINE A steam engine in which high-pressure steam expands and does work in a succession of cylinders or turbine chambers.

CONDUCTION, ELECTRICAL The transfer of electricity within a substance from points of higher to points of lower potential. Conductivity is usually measured by its inverse —resistivity. The unit of conductivity is the mho.

CONDUCTION, THERMAL The transfer of heat within a substance from points of higher to points of lower temperature.

COULOMB The unit of quantity of electricity, roughly 6×10^{18} electrons.

DAVY, SIR HUMPHRY (1778-1829) English chemist, born in Penzance, Cornwall. At first apprenticed to a surgeon, Davy devoted his spare time to chemistry, and became president of the Pneumatic Institute at Bristol before he was 20. He

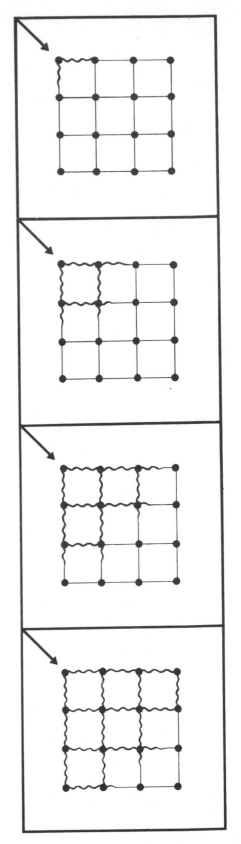

How heat travels through a poor conductor (one with no free electrons).

Missiles of War

In the 15th century, arrows were fired from grotesque attack towers (left). Crossbows (above) were more mobile, but it was a long step from these to today's rocket-propelled missiles launched from jet aircraft (below).

experimented with the effects of breathing certain gases, and he also tackled problems of tanning and agricultural chemistry. His researches in electrochemistry led to the isolation of sodium and potassium. Davy is also remembered for his invention of a miner's safety lamp, known as the *Davy lamp*, which greatly reduced the risk of firedamp explosions underground.

DC (DIRECT CURRENT) A flow of electricity from a point of greater to a point of lower potential (compare with AC). Few domestic and industrial consumers now use DC, because AC is safer, and cheaper to transform (see TRANSFORMER). But at very high voltages and over long distances, DC lines suffer fewer power losses than AC ones. DC lines carry power to Gotland from Sweden, which pioneered such systems, and between Britain and France.

DIESEL ENGINE A type of internal-combustion engine☞ that burns heavy oil and needs no spark to ignite the fuel. It works in the following way: (1) Air is introduced into the cylinders and compressed until it reaches a temperature above the ignition point of the fuel. (2) Fuel oil is sprayed into the air. (3) It is ignited by the high temperature and burned. (4) The pressure of the hot expanding gases pushes the piston downward. (5) The gases produced by combustion are evacuated through the exhaust valves.

DRAG The frictional resistance of air to the passage of a body through it. For instance, most of the air that flows past an aircraft does so in a smooth and streamlined manner, but immediately above the skin there are turbulent eddies and whorls.

The energy that goes into creating such eddies is taken from the forward motion of the aircraft. Drag therefore tends to increase the aircraft's fuel consumption. One way of reducing drag on the wings is to suck the layer of air around the wing into the jet intake.

DYNAMO An electric generator with a permanent magnet.

DYNE Unit of force; the force that will give a mass of 1 gm an acceleration of 1 cm/sec².

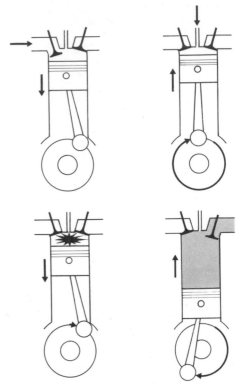

How a diesel engine works. (1) Piston draws in air. (2) Piston compresses air; fuel is injected. (3) The fuel ignites, and gases push piston down. (4) Waste gases are expelled.

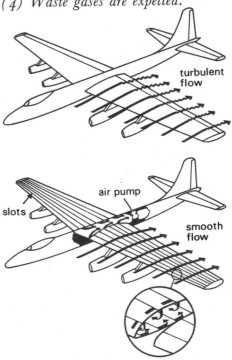

Drag (upper) may be reduced by slots that suck air through wing (lower).

Edison's electric light bulbs.

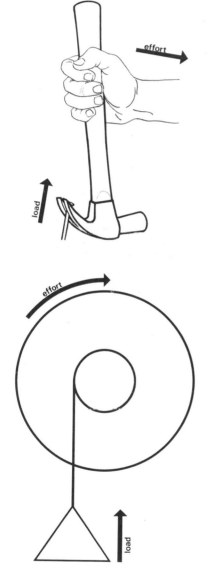

The mechanical advantage of a lever (upper) or a machine (lower) is the ratio between load and effort.

EDISON, THOMAS (1847-1931) American inventor, born in Ohio. Edison patented a total of 1093 inventions—more than any other man in American history. Among the most important were the incandescent electric light bulb (pp. 45-6), the phonograph, the movie projector, and an amplifier for Bell's telephone.

EFFORT The force needed to move a body.

ELECTRICITY The general name for all phenomena that arise out of the flow or accumulation of electrons in matter. The unit of quantity is the coulomb☞; that of pressure, the volt☞; and that of flow, the ampere☞.

ELECTROLYSIS The chemical decomposition of a substance when electricity is passed through it in solution or in the molten state (see CONDUCTION).

ELECTROMAGNET A temporary magnet made by winding a coil around a core of soft iron and passing a current through the coil. The magnetic field around the coil is enhanced by the iron, which becomes a magnet for as long as the current flows.

ELECTROMOTIVE FORCE (EMF) A measure of the intensity of electrical energy needed to produce a current in a circuit. The practical unit is the volt☞.

ELECTRON Elementary particle that orbits the atomic nucleus (see ATOM). The movement of electrons constitutes an electrical current.

ELECTRON VOLT (EV) A unit of energy used in nuclear physics; the energy used to raise an electron☞ through a potential of one volt☞.

ELEMENT In chemistry, a substance consisting entirely of atoms of the same atomic number☞.

ENERGY The capacity to do work. *Potential energy* arises by virtue of the position or configuration of matter: a pendulum at the top of its swing and a wound-up clock spring both have potential energy. *Kinetic energy* is energy of motion: flowing water, a pendulum in mid-stroke, a bullet in flight—these have kinetic energy. *Heat energy* is the kinetic energy of molecules. *Chemical energy* arises out of the capacity of atoms☞ to evolve heat as they combine or separate. *Electrical energy* arises out of the capacity of moving electrons☞ to evolve heat, electromagnetic radiation, and magnetic fields☞. *Nuclear energy* arises out of the elimination of all or part of the mass☞ of atomic particles. *Radiant energy* is energy in transit through space; it is emitted by electrons as they change orbit and by atomic nuclei during fission and fusion (see ATOM); on striking matter, such energy appears ultimately as heat. Only radiant energy can exist alone; all other forms require the presence of matter.

Some forms of energy can be converted into other forms, and all forms are ultimately converted into heat. Energy is measured in *ergs*— the same unit as for work.

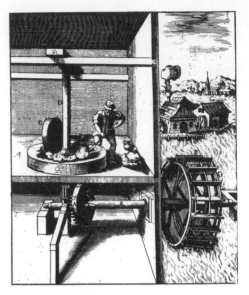

Watermill using the kinetic energy of a stream to grind corn.

ENGINE A device for turning energy of different kinds into kinetic energy☞, usually with the intention of putting it to work. An *electric engine*, or motor, uses the power of electric current to create a magnetic field. An *internal-combustion engine* works by converting chemical energy in gasoline or diesel-fuel molecules☞ into heat, which is then used to expand gases in a cylinder. The expanded gases drive a piston (as in a steam engine); the piston, in turn, drives a crankshaft.

Michael Faraday (1791-1867).

Faraday made a current flow through a wire by turning it inside a magnet.

FAHRENHEIT SCALE A temperature scale in which the boiling point of water is 212° and its freezing point 32°. These points were chosen by the originator of the scale, Gabriel Daniel Fahrenheit of Germany (1683-1736), in the mistaken belief that natural temperatures at the earth's surface would not fall below zero. To convert °F to °C, subtract 32, multiply by 5, and divide the product by 9.

FARADAY, MICHAEL (1791-1867) English physicist and chemist who became assistant to Humphry Davy☞ at the age of 21. In 1831 he announced his discovery of electromagnetic induction; shortly afterward he showed that the five known kinds of electricity☞ (frictional, galvanic, voltaic, magnetic, and thermal) were fundamentally the same. He also discovered the laws of electrolysis☞.

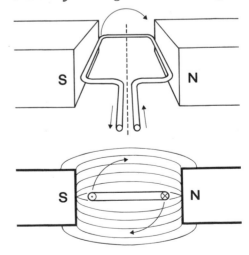

Power from Water *Primitive man did not see water as a source of power; to him it was simply a necessity for his crops. He used simple machines, driven by men or animals, to raise it and distribute it for irrigation. Later—and for many centuries—the power of streams and rivers was harnessed to drive waterwheels, but it is only very recently that water has become a major source of power. For years engineers tried—and failed—to harness the enormous power of the tides. Today, this source of energy is successfully exploited at the Rance tidal power station in France (below); it uses the tides to drive turbines, and may produce up to 540 million kilowatt hours per year.*

FORCE The push or pull that alters the motion of a moving body or moves a stationary body. The unit of force is the dyne☞ or the *poundal*☞.

FREEZING POINT The temperature at which a substance changes its state from liquid to solid.

FRICTION The force that resists the relative motion of two surfaces in contact with each other. It is proportional to the force (usually gravity) that holds the surfaces together.

GALILEI, GALILEO (1564-1642) Italian astronomer and physicist, born at Pisa. He discovered that all heavy compact bodies gain speed at almost exactly the same rate when falling through air, and he also discovered that the weight of a body is a product of its mass☞ and acceleration☞. He invented a pendulum clock, a basic thermometer, a proportional compass, and the first astronomical telescope. In 1633 he was condemned by the Inquisition for teaching that the sun was the center of the universe.

GALVANI, LUIGI (1737-98) Italian physician and physicist, born at Bologna. While lecturer in anatomy at Bologna University, Galvani experimented with the effect of two metals on a frog's legs (p. 38) and produced an electric current. He concluded, wrongly, that the current was generated by the frog's nerves. He also invented the first *galvanizing* process for protecting iron and steel against rust.

GAMMA RAYS (γ rays) Electromagnetic radiation similar to X rays☞. The names merely identify the radiation source: X rays come from electrical machines, gamma rays from nuclear fission☞.

GRAVITATION, NEWTON'S LAW OF Every particle in the universe attracts every other particle; the attraction between any two particles is proportional to their masses and inversely proportional to the square of the distance between them.

GUERICKE, OTTO VON (1602-86) German physicist, born in Magdeburg. He studied law and mathematics, and later became an engineer. Guericke experimented with the creation of a vacuum, and he invented the air pump. He built

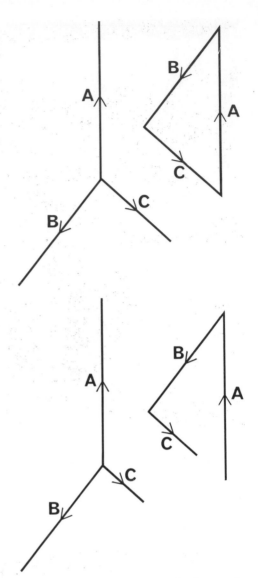

If three forces acting on a body can be represented as the sides of a triangle, they will be in equilibrium.

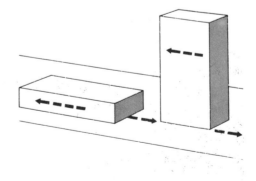

Friction is equal in both cases; it does not depend on surface area.

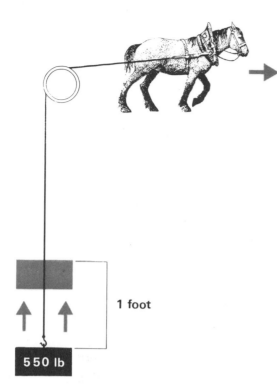

1 hp is the power needed to raise 550 lb through 1 ft in 1 sec.

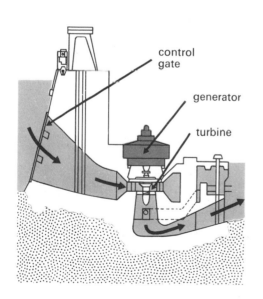

control gate

generator

turbine

Hydroelectric power station. Water flows down from dam (left) to turn turbine below generator; after use, it escapes through a tunnel (right).

an electrical machine that depended on friction applied to a rotating ball of sulfur (p. 37); and he also predicted (correctly) the intervals at which comets were due to reappear.

HORSEPOWER (hp) A unit of power; the power needed to raise 550 lb through 1 ft in 1 sec. Engines develop more hp the faster they run. So auto output ought always to be quoted, for example, 100 hp at 6000 rpm. To avoid confusion, auto engines are usually rated by their cubic capacity, which is directly proportional to their hp.

HYDROELECTRIC POWER Electrical energy obtained by using water power to drive a dynamo. See also TURBINE.

INERTIA The tendency of a body to resist force.

INSULATOR A substance in whose atoms the outer orbital electrons are so tightly bound that small potential difference will not cause the electrons to migrate. Good electrical insulators are usually good thermal insulators too (see CONDUCTION).

ISOTOPES Atoms of the same element that have the same atomic numbers☞ but different mass numbers (see ATOM). A radioisotope is a radioactive isotope made by exposing nonradioactive elements to radiation in a nuclear reactor☞.

JET PROPULSION The name given to forward motion produced by the discharge of a stream of liquid or gas at the rear. The four main types of jet engines used in aircraft are the turbojet, turboprop, pulse-jet, and ramjet☞.

JOLIOT-CURIE, FRÉDÉRIC (1900-58) French physicist, born in Paris. With his wife Irène he discovered three new radioactive elements—isotopes☞ of nitrogen, phosphorus, and aluminum. He also observed the emission of neutrons☞ in nuclear fission☞. In 1935 he and his wife were awarded the Nobel Prize for chemistry.

KEPLER, JOHANNES (1571-1630) German astronomer who discovered the relationship between the planets' periods of revolution and their distances from the sun (p. 21). He also found that the planets follow elliptical orbits with the sun at one of their foci; and that the speed of a planet in its orbit varies according to its distance from the sun.

KINETIC ENERGY See ENERGY

LEVER A rigid bar turning on a fixed point of support called the *fulcrum*, generally used for raising weights (see also p. 9).

LOAD (1) The force available at the business end of a lever☞. (2) The energy tapped from any power source.

MAGNETIC FIELD The field of force that exists around electrons☞ traveling along a conductor or orbiting the atomic nucleus.

MASS A basic property of matter, for everyday purposes identical with weight. But even when objects become weightless (for example, in earth orbit), they lose none of their mass—they still have inertia and momentum. For the nuclear physicist, mass and energy are interchangeable (see ATOM). There are two ways of determining the mass of a body. One is to weigh it and apply Newton's Law (see GRAVITATION). The other is to apply a force☞ to it and to calculate the mass from the resulting acceleration☞.

MECHANICAL ADVANTAGE (1) Of a lever☞: the ratio between the load and the effort. (2) Of a machine: the ratio between the load raised at a given constant speed and the force required to keep the machine at that speed.

MECHANICS The study of how matter behaves under the influence of force.

MODERATOR A substance used in a nuclear reactor☞ in order to slow down, or *moderate*, fast neutrons☞. Such neutrons might otherwise escape from the reactor or be captured by unsuitable atoms. The moderator slows the neutrons down until they reach an appropriate speed for triggering further chain reactions☞.

MOLECULAR WEIGHT The sum of the atomic weights of all the atoms in a molecule☞.

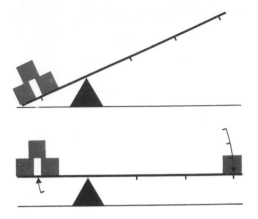

The principle of the lever: a 1-lb weight 3 ft from the fulcrum will raise 3 lb 1 ft from the fulcrum.

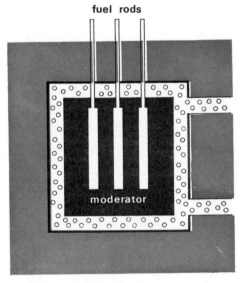

Graphite-moderated reactor.

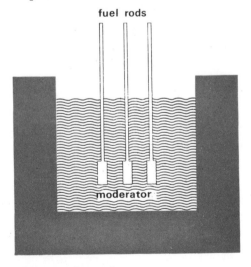

Water-moderated reactor.

Machine Transport

In the 1830s, steam locomotives pulled early passenger trains (top). Less than 60 years later came the internal-combustion engine, which enabled Ford to build his first automobile (above). Today's developments include hover-craft (right) and hovertrain (below).

MOLECULE The smallest part of a substance that can exist separately while still having the chemical properties of the original substance.

MOMENTUM The measure of the motion of a body, determined by multiplying its mass☞ by its velocity☞.

MOTION, NEWTON'S LAWS OF (1) A body at rest remains at rest unless an external force acts on it; a body in motion continues to move uniformly and in a straight line unless an external force acts on it. (2) An external force that acts on a body changes that body's momentum; the rate at which the momentum changes is proportional to the force; the change takes place in the direction of the force. (3) To every action there is an equal and opposite reaction.

NEUTRON An elementary particle found in almost all nuclei (see ATOM).

NEWTON, SIR ISAAC (1642-1727) British physicist and mathematician. He discovered the nature of gravity, and concluded that it was the same force as the force that kept the planets in motion. He also invented differential calculus, and formulated the corpuscular theory of light. See also GRAVITATION; MOTION.

NUCLEAR FISSION A nuclear reaction in which a heavy and unstable atomic nucleus (i.e. the nucleus of any element with atomic number 84 or greater) splits into approximately equal parts, emitting neutrons, radiation, and heat energy (see ATOM). The neutrons may trigger further fission and so set up a chain reaction☞.

NUCLEAR FUSION A nuclear reaction in which two light atomic nuclei fuse, or combine, to form one heavier nucleus, emitting particles, radiation, and heat energy. Such fusion reactions are the basis of the hydrogen bomb, and of our hopes for cheap and unlimited electrical power from the atom.

NUCLEAR REACTOR A device in which a nuclear-fission chain reaction is maintained at a controlled rate. Most are used as heat sources to raise steam for electricity generation.

Isaac Newton, and his diagram of the basic laws governing space travel.

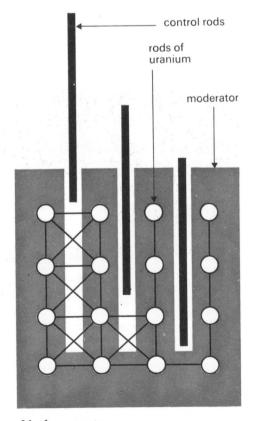

control rods

rods of uranium

moderator

Nuclear reactor.

Radar screen and control unit.

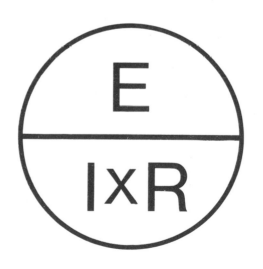

Resistance (R) equals potential difference (E) divided by current (I). (Cover up the quantity you want, and the formula for working it out is left.)

OHM The unit that defines the resistance☞ of a conductor to electric current.

POTENTIAL ENERGY See ENERGY.

POUNDAL Unit of force: the force needed to give a mass of one pound an acceleration of 1 ft/sec².

POWER A measure of the rate of doing work (see HORSEPOWER; WATT).

PRESSURE A measure of force per unit area; expressed in pounds per square inch (psi) or grams per square centimeter (gm/cm²).

PROTON An elementary particle found in all nuclei (see ATOM).

RADAR Any locating, navigating, or guiding system that employs microwaves. The word "radar" is an abbreviation of the phrase "radio detection and ranging." Radar works independently of weather and visibility conditions because it depends on the ability of microwaves to bounce back from solid objects.

RADIOACTIVITY The spontaneous fission of the atomic nucleus accompanied by the emission of alpha or beta radiation (and sometimes of gamma radiation, too).

RAMJET ENGINE A simple type of jet propulsion☞ system. The engine has a continuous inlet of air in its forward end, so that air is taken in and compressed only by the forward motion of the vehicle.

RESISTANCE Except for certain materials at low temperatures, all conductors of electricity resist the flow of current, turning some of it into heat.
Resistance depends on the cross section of the conductor (the smaller the cross section, the greater the resistance), and its temperature (the hotter it is, the greater its resistance).

ROCKET A projectile driven by jet propulsion☞ and containing its own fuel and propellants. Because rockets do not rely on air, they provide a means of propulsion outside the earth's atmosphere. They may be powered either by nuclear reactor☞ or by solid or liquid fuels. Space rockets are constructed in separate sections to enable them to escape the earth's gravitational field. The first section, or *booster*, provides sufficient thrust to propel the rocket up to the thinner regions of the atmosphere; at that stage it is jettisoned, and the propulsion is taken over by another section. The process is repeated, so that the rocket gradually becomes lighter as it moves farther away from the earth. *Retro-rockets*, which produce thrust in the opposite direction to the main rocket, are used to slow the projectile down before a landing.

RUTHERFORD, ERNEST (1871-1937) British physicist, born in New Zealand, who won the Nobel Prize for chemistry in 1908. He discovered alpha rays and beta rays, and he later showed that alpha particles consist of helium atoms. He also succeeded in transmuting the element nitrogen into an isotope☞ of oxygen by bombarding it with alpha particles.

SATELLITES, ARTIFICIAL   Man-made vehicles designed to orbit the earth, moon, or any other heavenly body. The first artificial satellite was launched into orbit around the earth by Russia in 1957. Satellites are used to obtain and radio back to earth information about conditions in the upper atmosphere, the ionosphere, and outer space. Communication satellites, such as *Telstar* and *Early Bird*, are used for relaying radio and television signals around the curved surface of the earth. Their instruments are powered by solar cell batteries☞.

SOLAR CELL BATTERY An electric cell that converts energy from the sun into electrical energy.

SONIC BOOM The explosive noise produced by an aircraft or missile traveling at supersonic speed. The pressure waves ahead of an aircraft travel at the speed of sound. When the aircraft overtakes them, a shock-wave cone is created at its nose, and this produces a noise that is heard at a number of points on the ground.

SPECIFIC HEAT OF A SUBSTANCE The quantity of heat (in calories) needed to raise one gram of the substance through 1° C.

Telstar.

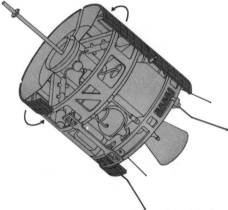
Solar cells and batteries (black) in a communications satellite.

Early Bird.

90

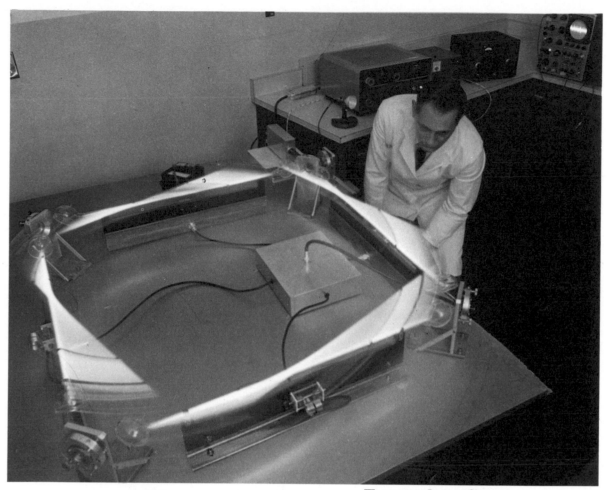

Energy from Gas

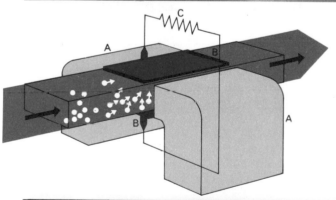

Experiments with ring lasers (above) have produced more accurate guidance systems for ships. Magnetohydrodynamic generation may enable us to tap a new energy source—hot, ionized gases (below). Diagram, left, shows how the poles of a magnet (A) might be used to charge gases with electric currents, to be tapped by electrodes (B). Motor (C) represents resistance.

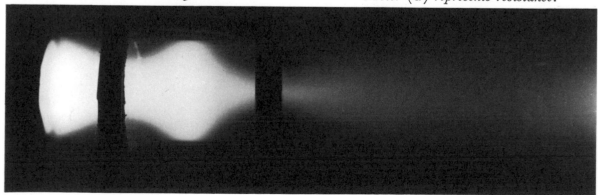

SPEED The ratio of distance covered to the time taken to cover it by a moving body.

STEPHENSON, GEORGE (1781-1848) English inventor and founder of railroads, born at Wylam, Northumberland. Stephenson's first invention was a steam locomotive, produced for the colliery where he worked. Its special feature was a cylinder and piston device that attached the wheels to the body of the locomotive, and prevented them from slipping on the tracks.

THERM Unit of heat; 100,000 British thermal units.

THERMODYNAMICS The general study of energy processes, particularly those that involve heat.

TORRICELLI, EVANGELISTA (1608-47) Italian physicist and mathematician, born at Faenza. Torricelli was the first to prove that air has weight (p. 17). He also investigated fluid motion, and wrote on the theory of projectiles.

TRANSFORMER A device for changing AC at one voltage into AC of the same frequency at another voltage. The typical transformer consists of an iron core (a bar or a loop) around which are wound two coils—a primary (or input) coil and a secondary (or output) coil. AC in the primary coil creates a fluctuating magnetic field in the core, which induces AC of the same frequency in the secondary coil.

TRANSISTOR A small, long-lasting device for amplifying electrical signals; it is dependent on the special qualities of germanium and silicon crystals as semiconductors.

TURBINE A motor with a shaft rotated steadily by jets of steam, air, water, or other fluid striking the blades of a wheel. The Francis reaction turbine is the most common kind used in hydro-electric schemes. Its rate of rotation can be kept constant under varying loads by adjusting the guide vanes that direct the water onto the turbine itself; this makes it ideal for electricity generation.

VELOCITY Rate of motion in a given direction.

George Stephenson (1781-1848).

Stephenson's Rocket.

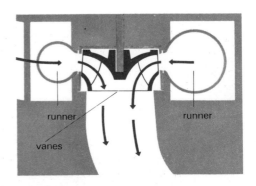

Francis reaction turbine.

Alessandro Volta (1745-1827).

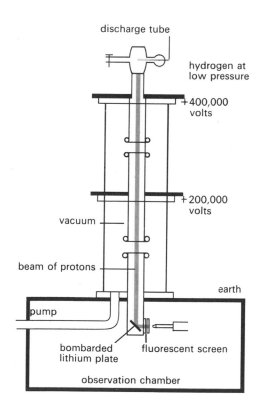

discharge tube

hydrogen at low pressure

+400,000 volts

+200,000 volts

vacuum

beam of protons

earth

pump

bombarded lithium plate

fluorescent screen

observation chamber

Diagram of the discharge tube used by Cockcroft and Walton to split the nucleus of the lithium atom.

VOLT Unit of electromotive force or of potential difference. A difference of 1 volt potential across the ends of a conductor whose resistance is 1 ohm causes a current of 1 ampere to flow.

VOLTA, ALESSANDRO (1745-1827) Italian physicist and pioneer of electrical science, born at Como. Volta invented the cell, pile, and battery that bear his name (p. 38). His name was also given to the *volt*☞.

WALTON, ERNEST THOMAS (1903-) Irish physicist who succeeded (with his colleague Sir John Cockcroft☞) in splitting the nucleus of the lithium atom by bombarding it with artificially accelerated protons. For this achievement, they were jointly awarded the 1951 Nobel Prize for physics.

WATT A unit of power; the capacity to do work at the rate of 10^7 ergs/sec.

WATT, JAMES (1736-1819) Scottish inventor, born at Greenock. After working as an instrument maker, he designed a new and more economical steam engine with a separate condenser, which replaced the Newcomen model. His later inventions adapted the engine to drive machinery of many different kinds.

WORK In physics, "work" is done only when a force moves a mass through a vertical distance. Thus a man who rows all day on a calm lake does no work on the boat—until he pulls it up the beach for the night. If the boat (which weighs, say, 300 lb) finally rests 4 ft above water level, the man does 4×300, that is 1200, ft lb of work on it. Work is distinct from energy (the capacity to do work) and power (the rate of doing work).

X RAYS Electromagnetic radiation of the same kind as light but with much shorter wavelength. X rays are produced when beams of high-speed electrons strike matter, or when high-energy orbital electrons lose energy and fall to a lower orbit. Flesh is transparent to X rays, and since X rays affect photographic plates in the same way as light, they make it possible to photograph bones within the body.

Index

Picture Credits

28 (BL) Mansell Collection
   (BR) Science Museum, London
29 Science Museum, London
30 Peter Warner
31 Photos Axel Poignant
32 Peter Warner
33 Keystone
35 Courtesy of C. A. Parsons & Co. Ltd.
36 Science Museum, London
38 (TL) Peter Warner
   (TR) Mansell Collection
39 (BL) Science Museum, London
   (BR) British Museum/Photo John Webb
40 Mary Evans Picture Library
41 (BL&BR) Viners of Sheffield
43 (T) British Steel Corporation/Photo John Hedgecoe
43 (B) British Museum/Photo John Webb
44 Peter Warner
45 Photo Ken Coton
46-47 Diagram Michael Mellish and Walter Greaves
   (BR) Photo Geoffrey Drury
48 The English Electric Company Limited
49 Peter Warner
51 (TL) Science Museum, London/Photo John Freeman
   (TR/CR/BR) Peter Warner
52 Science Museum, London/Photo John Webb
57 (T&C) Mansell Collection
   (B) Courtesy The London Library
   Diagrams Peter Warner
59 Peter Warner
60 (BL) Gillian Newing
   (BR) Gernsheim Collection, The University of Texas at Austin
61 (B&BR) Bristol Siddeley Engines Ltd·
63 (BC) Joan Freeman
65 (C) David Litchfield
   (B) Peter Warner
67 (T) United States Information Service
   (B) Photo N. R. Farbman, *Life* magazine © 1968 Time Inc.
70 Official Department of Defense Photograph
72 E.N.E.L., Compartimento di Firenze
73 (CL) Gordon Cramp
   (BL) John Messenger
   (BR) Endfield Cable Company

74 Atelier Andre Steiner
76 (TR) Mansell Collection
   Diagrams Peter Warner
77 (TL) Peter Warner
   (BL) Mansell Collection
78 Peter Warner
79 (TR) British Museum/Photo John Webb
   (BC) Official Department of Defense Photograph
80 (TR) Peter Warner
81 (TL) Mansell Collection
   (BL) Peter Warner
82 (CR) Mansell Collection
   (BR) Peter Warner
83 (T) Photo J. Allan Cash
   (B) Electricité de France, Paris
84 (TR&BR) Peter Warner
85 (TL) Peter Warner
   (BL) John Messenger
86 Diagrams Peter Warner
87 (T) Museum of British Transport
   (CR) Keystone
   (B) Daily Telegraph Magazine/Photo John Marmaras
88 (TR) Mansell Collection
89 (TL) Courtesy of The Marconi Company Ltd.
   (BL) Peter Warner
90 (TR) Keystone
   (CR) Ian Kestle
   (BR) United States Information Service
91 (TC) Electro Optics Group, Sperry Rand Corporation, New York
   (BL) Culham Laboratory, United Kingdom Atomic Energy Authority
92 (TR&CR) Mansell Collection
   (BR) Gillian Newing
93 (TL) Science Museum, London
   (BL) Dr. T. E. Allibone, C.B.E., F.R.S., *The Release and Use of Atomic Energy*, Chapman & Hall Ltd., London, 1961